Collins

A2 RevisionNotes
Maths

Ted Graham • John Berry

Series editor: Jayne de Courcy

William Collins' dream of knowledge for all began with the publication of his first book in 1819. A self-educated mill worker, he not only enriched millions of lives, but also founded a flourishing publishing house. Today, staying true to this spirit, Collins books are packed with inspiration, innovation and practical expertise. They place you at the centre of a world of possibility and give you exactly what you need to explore it.

Collins. Do more.

Published by Collins
An imprint of HarperCollins*Publishers*
77 – 85 Fulham Palace Road
Hammersmith
London
W6 8JB

Browse the complete Collins catalogue at
www.collinseducation.com

© HarperCollins*Publishers* Limited 2006

10 9 8 7 6 5 4 3 2 1

ISBN-13 978 0 00 720692 6
ISBN-10 0 00 720692 5

British Library Cataloguing in Publication Data
A Catalogue record for this publication is available from the British Library.

Edited by Karen Westall
Production by Katie Butler
Series design by Sally Boothroyd
Book design by Jerry Fowler and Ken Vail Graphic Design
Illustrations by Jerry Fowler
Index compiled by Julie Rimington
Printed and bound by Printing Express, Hong Kong

You might also like to visit
www.harpercollins.co.uk
The book lover's website

CONTENTS

HOW THIS BOOK WILL HELP YOU

We have planned this book to make your revision as easy and effective as possible.

Here's how:

SHORT, ACCESSIBLE NOTES THAT YOU CAN INTEGRATE INTO YOUR REVISION FILE

Collins Revision Notes A2 Maths has been prepared by top examiners who know exactly what you need to revise in order to achieve a top grade.

You can *either* revise entirely from this book *or* you can tear off the notes and integrate them into your own revision file. This will ensure that you have the best possible notes to revise from.

STUDENT-FRIENDLY PRESENTATION

The notes have been designed to make your revision as easy as possible:

- Short lists at the start of each unit give key points and definitions.

MUST REMEMBER ...

Blue panels highlight particularly key content.

GIVEN FORMULAE ...

Green panels contain relevant formulae that can be found in the formula book.

EXAMPLE

- **Yellow panels** contain examplar exam questions with solutions beneath them.

CONTENT MATCHED TO YOUR SPECIFICATION

There are small coloured boxes down the side of each unit indicating to which specifications and modules it is relevant. This means that you can see at a glance which units you need to revise in order to cover your particular specification.

This book covers all of A2 Core Maths 3 and 4. To complete your A2 course, you can choose additional Decision Maths, Mechanics or Statistics option modules from the AS specification. To revise these, you will need *Collins Revision Notes AS Maths*.

GUIDANCE ON EXAM TECHNIQUE

Each short unit contains one or more typical exam questions. Solutions are given to these, along with step-by-step guidance on how to arrive at the correct answer.

If you want more help with exam technique, use the exam practice book alongside these Revision Notes: *Collins Do Brilliantly A2 Maths*.

Using both these books will help you to achieve a high grade in your A2 Maths exams.

DEFINITION OF A FUNCTION I

KEY POINTS AND DEFINITIONS

- A function is a one-to-one or a many-to-one mapping from a set of values called the domain to a set of values called the range or co-domain.

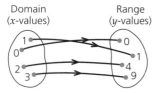 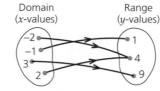

The function f: $x \rightarrow x^2$ for $x \geq 0$ is a one-to-one mapping.

The function f: $x \rightarrow x^2$ for the set of real numbers is a many-to-one mapping.

- Each member in the domain has a corresponding image value in the range.

- A function is often written as, for example, f: $x \rightarrow 3x^2 + 1$ or f$(x) = 3x^2 + 1$.

EXAMPLE

- For each of the following functions, with given domain:

  (a) draw a mapping diagram;

  (b) state whether the function is one-to-one or many-to-one.

  (i) f: $x \rightarrow 10 - 3x$ $\{x: -2, 0, 1, 4\}$

  (ii) f: $x \rightarrow 2x^2 + 1$ $\{x: -3, -1, 1, 3\}$

  (iii) f: $x \rightarrow x^3 + 9x$ $\{x: -3, 0, 3\}$

SOLUTION

(i) (a) 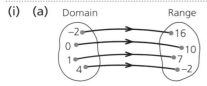 (b) The function is one-to-one	In each case the function only exists for the given x-values. This is an example of a linear function.
(ii) (a) 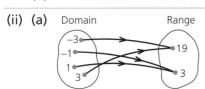 (b) The function is many-to-one	This is an example of a quadratic function.
(iii) (a) 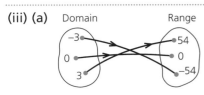 (b) The function is one-to-one	This is an example of a cubic function.

AQA C3
Edexcel C3
OCR C3
OCR(MEI) C3
WJEC C3

DEFINITION OF A FUNCTION II

KEY POINTS AND DEFINITIONS

- If a mapping is a function, a graph can be drawn.

EXAMPLE

- For each of the following functions, with given domain:

  (a) sketch a graph of the function;

  (b) state whether the function is one-to-one or many-to-one.

  (i) $f(x) = 2 + 5x$ $\{x: -2 \leq x \leq 2\}$

  (ii) $f(x) = \dfrac{1}{2}x^2 + 1$ $\{x: -5 \leq x \leq 5\}$

  (iii) $f(x) = \dfrac{3}{x}$ $\{x \in \mathfrak{R} \leq x \neq 0\}$

SOLUTION

(i) (a)

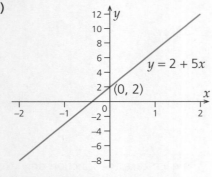

(b) The function is one-to-one

Linear functions have straight line graphs.

(ii) (a)

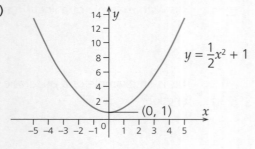

(b) The function is many-to-one

The graph of a quadratic function is called a parabola.

(iii) (a)

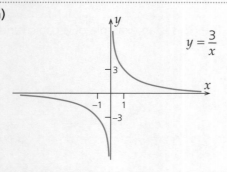

(b) The function is one-to-one

For this function the x- and y-axes are asymptotes.

DOMAIN AND RANGE OF A FUNCTION

KEY POINTS AND DEFINITIONS

- The set of object values for which a function is defined is called the domain. The set of image values is called the range (or co-domain).

EXAMPLE 1

- The functions f, g and h are defined by:

  f: $x \rightarrow 3x - 1$ $\{x: x \geq 1\}$
  g: $x \rightarrow x^2 + 1$ $\{x: x \in \mathfrak{R}\}$

  h: $x \rightarrow \dfrac{3x}{x - 2}$ $\{x: x > 2\}$

  (a) Find the range of each function.

  (b) State whether the function is one-to-one or many-to-one.

SOLUTION

For f: $x \rightarrow 3x - 1$ $f(1) = 2$ and $f(x)$ is increasing. The range for f is $\{y: y \geq 2\}$ The function is one-to-one	To find the range of a function, consider all the possible values that could be produced by the function.
The range for g is $\{y: y \geq 1\}$ because $x^2 \geq 0$. The function is many-to-one	
The graph of the function h is: The range of the function h is $\{y: y > 3\}$ The function is one-to-one 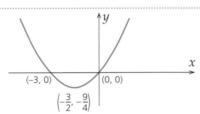	Often a sketch of the graph of the function helps to find the range. Efficient use of a graphic calculator will help.

EXAMPLE 2

- The function $f(x) = x^2 + 3x$ with domain $\{x: x \in \mathfrak{R}, x \geq p\}$ is one-to-one. Find the least value of p and sketch the graph of this function.

SOLUTION

The function $f(x)$ is symmetrical about the point $\left(-\dfrac{3}{2}, 0\right)$ 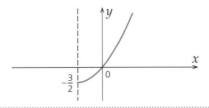	Sketch the graph of $f(x) = x^2 + 3x$.
The function $f(x)$ is one-to-one for $x \geq -\dfrac{3}{2}$ so $p = -\dfrac{3}{2}$ A sketch of the function is:	As $x \geq p$, the right-hand half of the graph is needed.

EXAMPLE 3

- The diagram shows a graph of the curve with equation $y = f(x)$.

  Write down the domain and range of the function.

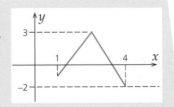

SOLUTION

The domain of the function is $\{x: 1 \leq x \leq 4\}$	Possible values for x.
The range of the function is $\{y: -2 \leq y \leq 3\}$	Possible values for y.

COMPOSITE FUNCTIONS

AQA
C3

Edexcel
C33

OCR
C3

OCR(MEI)
C3

WJEC
C3

KEY POINTS AND DEFINITIONS

- A composite function is a combination of functions in which one function is followed by another: $fg(x) \equiv f(g(x))$

EXAMPLE 1

- The functions f and g are defined as:

$$f: x \rightarrow x - 3 \quad x \in \mathfrak{R} \qquad\qquad g: x \rightarrow 4x^2 \quad x \in \mathfrak{R}$$

(a) State the range of g.

(b) Find $gf(4)$ and $fg(4)$.

(c) Find $gf(x)$ and $fg(x)$. State the range of each of these composite functions.

(d) For what values of x does $gf(x) = fg(x)$?

SOLUTION

(a) The range of g is $g(x) \geq 0$ as $x^2 \geq 0$	
(b) $gf(4) = g(4 - 3) = g(1) = 4(1^2) = 4$ $fg(4) = f(4 \times 4^2) = f(64) = 64 - 3 = 61$	To find $gf(4)$ first find $f(4)$ and then apply g to the result.
(c) $gf(x) = g(x - 3) = 4(x - 3)^2$ Range of $gf(x)$ is $\{y: y \geq 0\}$ $fg(x) = f(4x^2) = 4x^2 - 3$ Range of $fg(x)$ is $\{y: y \geq -3\}$ as $4x^2 \geq 0$	Must remember that squared term cannot be negative.
(d) $\quad 4(x - 3)^2 = 4x^2 - 3$ $4(x^2 - 6x + 9) = 4x^2 - 3 \Rightarrow -24x + 36 = -3 \Rightarrow 24x = 39$ $\qquad\qquad x = \dfrac{13}{8}$ There is one value of x for which $fg(x) = gf(x)$	Expand left-hand side and simplify.

EXAMPLE 2

- Functions f, g and h are defined by:

$$f: x \rightarrow 8 - x \quad g: x \rightarrow \frac{3}{x} \ (x \neq 0) \quad h: x \rightarrow 2x + 3$$

(a) Find expressions for $gf(x)$, $hg(x)$, $fh(x)$ and $hh(x)$.

(b) Show that $ff(x) = x$ and $gg(x) = x$.

(c) Solve the equation $hgf(x) = x$.

SOLUTION

(a) $gf(x) = g(8 - x) = \dfrac{3}{8 - x} \qquad hg(x) = h\left(\dfrac{3}{x}\right) = \dfrac{6}{x} + 3$ $fh(x) = f(2x + 3) = 5 - 2x$ $hh(x) = h(2x + 3) = 2(2x + 3) + 3 = 4x + 9$	Express the composite functions as simply as possible.
(b) $ff(x) = f(8 - x) = 8 - (8 - x) = x \qquad gg(x) = g\left(\dfrac{3}{x}\right) = \dfrac{3}{\frac{3}{x}} = x$	f and g have self-inverses.
(c) $hgf(x) = h\left(\dfrac{3}{8 - x}\right) = 2\left(\dfrac{3}{8 - x}\right) + 3 = \dfrac{6}{8 - x} + 3$ Thus when $hgf(x) = x$ $\qquad \dfrac{6}{8 - x} + 3 = x$ $\qquad\qquad 6 = (x - 3)(8 - x) \Rightarrow x^2 - 11x + 30 = 0$ $(x - 5)(x - 6) = 0 \quad x = 5$ or $x = 6$	Rearrange to form a quadratic equation.

INVERSE FUNCTIONS

KEY POINTS AND DEFINITIONS

- If f is a one-to-one function, then the function f^{-1} is the inverse of f if:

$$ff^{-1}(x) = f^{-1}f(x) = x$$

EXAMPLE 1

- The functions f and g are defined by:

$$f(x) = 2x - 1 \qquad x \in \mathfrak{R}$$

$$g(x) = e^x + 2 \qquad x \in \mathfrak{R}$$

(a) State the ranges of $f(x)$ and $g(x)$.

(b) Find $f^{-1}(x)$ and $g^{-1}(x)$.

(c) State the ranges of $f^{-1}(x)$ and $g^{-1}(x)$.

SOLUTION

(a) The range of $f(x)$ is $\{y: y \in \mathfrak{R}\}$

The range of $g(x)$ is $\{y: y \in \mathfrak{R}, y > 2\}$

> As $e^x > 0$ for all values of x, the range can be found.

(b) To find $f^{-1}(x)$: $\quad y = 2x - 1 \Rightarrow y + 1 = 2x$

$$x = \frac{y + 1}{2}$$

Then $f^{-1}: x \rightarrow \dfrac{x + 1}{2} \qquad x \in \mathfrak{R}$

> To find the inverse $f^{-1}(x)$, write $y = f(x)$ and solve for x. Then replace y by x and write $f^{-1}(x)$ as a function. Note that the domain of f^{-1} is the range of f.

To find $g^{-1}(x)$: $\quad y = e^x + 2 \Rightarrow e^x = y - 2$

$$x = \ln(y - 2)$$

Then $g^{-1}: x \rightarrow \ln(x - 2) \qquad x \in \mathfrak{R}, x > 2$

> Similarly for $g^{-1}(x)$.

(c) The range of $f^{-1}(x)$ is $\{y: y \in \mathfrak{R}\}$

The range of $g^{-1}(x)$ is $\{y: y \in \mathfrak{R}\}$

EXAMPLE 2

- For the function $f(x) = \dfrac{2x}{5 - x}$, the domain is $\{x: x \in \mathfrak{R}, x \neq a\}$.

(a) Find the value of a.

(b) Find the inverse function $f^{-1}(x)$.

(c) Write down the domain of f^{-1} and hence the range of f.

SOLUTION

(a) $\quad a = 5$

> Equate the denominator to zero.

(b) $\quad y = \dfrac{2x}{5 - x}$

$(5 - x)y = 2x$

$5y = xy + 2x$

$x = \dfrac{5y}{y + 2}$

$f^{-1}(x) = \dfrac{5x}{x + 2}$

> Reversing the role of x and y gives the function in the form $f^{-1}: x \rightarrow \dfrac{5x}{x + 2}$.

(c) The domain of f^{-1} is $\{x: x \in \mathfrak{R}, x \neq -2\}$ which is also the range for f.

GRAPHS OF FUNCTIONS AND THEIR INVERSES

AQA C3

Edexcel C3

OCR C3

OCR(MEI) C3

WJEC C3

KEY POINTS AND DEFINITIONS

- The graph of f^{-1} is a reflection of the graph of f in the line $y = x$.

EXAMPLE 1

- The diagram shows the graph of $y = \frac{x^2}{4}(6 - x)$.

The coordinates of the points A and B are (4, 8) and (6, 0) respectively.

Functions f and g are defined as follows:

f: $x \to \frac{x^2}{4}(6 - x)$, $0 \le x \le 4$ g: $x \to \frac{x^2}{4}(6 - x)$, $0 \le x \le 6$

(a) Explain why f has an inverse while g does not.

(b) State the domain and range of f^{-1} and sketch the graph of f^{-1}.

SOLUTION

(a) f is a one-to-one mapping and so has an inverse

g is a many-to-one mapping and so does not have an inverse

(b) Domain of f is $0 \le x \le 4$, range of f is $0 \le y \le 8$

Domain of f^{-1} is $0 \le x \le 8$, range of f^{-1} is $0 \le y \le 4$ The graph of f^{-1} is:

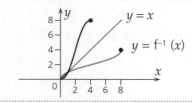

EXAMPLE 2

- For the function f: $x \to 2 - 4x - x^2$, the domain is $\{x: x \ge k\}$.

(a) Find the least value of k such that f is a one-to-one mapping and state the range of f in this case.

(b) Assuming the value of k found in part (a), find the inverse function, f^{-1}.

(c) Sketch a graph showing both $y = f(x)$ and $y = f^{-1}(x)$. State the equation of the line of symmetry for your graphs.

SOLUTION

(a) $f(x) = 6 - (2 + x)^2$

f is a one-to-one mapping if $x \ge -2$ so that $k = -2$

The range of f is $\{y: y \le 6\}$

For quadratics, complete the square to find the axis of symmetry. Sketch the graph of $y = 2 - 4x - x^2$.

(b) $y = 6 - (2 + x)^2$

$(2 + x)^2 = 6 - y \Rightarrow 2 + x = \pm\sqrt{6 - y} \Rightarrow x = -2 + \sqrt{6 - y}$

f^{-1}: $x \to -2 + \sqrt{6 - x}$ $\{x: x \le 6\}$

Rearrange to make x the subject. Choose the positive value since $x \ge -2$.

Must not confuse the symbol used for the variable.

(c) The line of symmetry is $y = x$

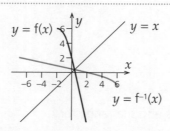

THE MODULUS FUNCTION AND ITS GRAPH

KEY POINTS AND DEFINITIONS

- The modulus of a number is its absolute value, i.e. its magnitude ignoring the sign.

- The magnitude (modulus) of x is denoted by $|x|$.

- The modulus function f: $x \to |x|$, $\{x: x \in \Re\}$ is a many-to-one mapping with range $\{y: y \in \Re, y \geq 0\}$ where

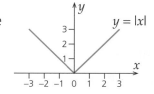

$$|x| = \begin{cases} x \text{ if } \geq 0 \\ -x \text{ if } < 0 \end{cases}$$

EXAMPLE 1

- Each of the following functions has domain $\{x: -2, -1, 0, 1, 2, 3, 4\}$. For each one draw a mapping diagram, state the range and whether the mapping is one-to-one or many-to-one.

f: $x \to |2x + 1|$

g: $x \to |2x + 5|$

SOLUTION

The range for f is $\{y: 1, 3, 5, 7, 9\}$, f is many-to-one

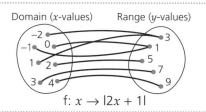

The range for g is $\{y: 1, 3, 5, 7, 9, 11, 13\}$, g is one-to-one

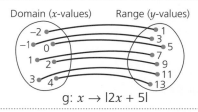

EXAMPLE 2

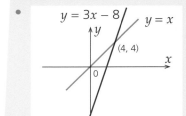

The diagram shows the graphs of the lines $y = x$ and $y = 3x - 8$ and their point of intersection $(4, 4)$. Sketch on a single diagram the graphs of $y = |x|$ and $y = |3x - 8|$ and find the points of intersection of these graphs.

SOLUTION

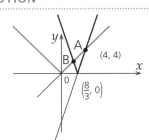

For A: $x = 4$ and $y = 4$ as before

For B: $x = 2$ and $y = 2$

The points of intersection are given by the intersection of the graphs $y = x$ and $y = 3x - 8$ (point A) and the graphs of $y = x$ and $y = 8 - 3x$ (point B).

EQUATIONS WITH THE MODULUS FUNCTION

KEY POINTS AND DEFINITIONS

- Must remember that a modulus function is always positive so its graph cannot be below the x-axis.

EXAMPLE 1

- If $f(x) = 2x - 4$,

    (a) sketch the graph of $y = |f(x)|$;

    (b) solve the equation $x = |f(x)|$.

SOLUTION

(a)

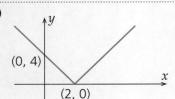

$$|f(x)| = \begin{cases} 2x - 4 & \text{if } x \geq 2 \\ 4 - 2x & \text{if } x < 2 \end{cases}$$

(0, 4)

(2, 0)

$f(x) > 0$ if $x > 2$ and $f(x) < 0$ if $x < 2$. The graph consists of two straight lines. The function is defined in two different ways either side of $x = 2$. The important points to indicate are where the function crosses the axes.

(b) If $x \geq 2$ we have

$x = 2x - 4$

$x = 4$

If $x < 2$ we have

$x = 4 - 2x$

$x = \dfrac{4}{3}$

So $x = 4$ or $\dfrac{4}{3}$

Both the cases where $x \geq 2$ and $x < 2$ must be considered because these will produce two different equations and hence two different values of x.

EXAMPLE 2

- (a) Sketch the graphs of $y = |x - 3|$ and $y = |2x + 1|$.

    (b) Solve the equation $|x - 3| = |2x + 1|$.

SOLUTION

(a)

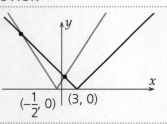

$\left(-\dfrac{1}{2}, 0\right)$ (3, 0)

Identify which parts of each graph intersect.

(b) $|x - 3| = |2x + 1|$,

either $2x + 1 = 3 - x$

$3x = 2$

$x = \dfrac{2}{3}$

or $-2x - 1 = 3 - x$

$x = -4$

So $x = -4$ or $\dfrac{2}{3}$

For $|x - 3|$, choose $y = 3 - x$ and for $|2x + 1|$, choose $y = 2x + 1$ for the positive value of x.

For the second solution, choose $y = 3 - x$ for $|x - 3|$ and choose $y = -2x - 1$ for $|2x + 1|$.

State both values of x.

COMBINATIONS OF TRANSFORMATIONS I

KEY POINTS AND DEFINITIONS

- If a graph has equation $y = f(x)$ and a is a constant, then:
  - $y = f(x) \pm a$ is a translation of a units parallel to the y-axis;
  - $y = f(x \pm a)$ is a translation of a units parallel to the x-axis;
  - $y = af(x)$ is a stretch parallel to the y-axis with a scale factor of a;
  - $y = f(ax)$ is a stretch parallel to the x-axis with a scale factor of $\frac{1}{a}$.

EXAMPLE 1

- The diagram shows the graph which has equation $y = f(x)$.

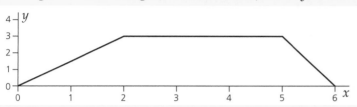

(a) Draw the graph of $y = 3f(x)$.

(b) Draw the graph of $y = f(2x)$.

SOLUTION

(a)
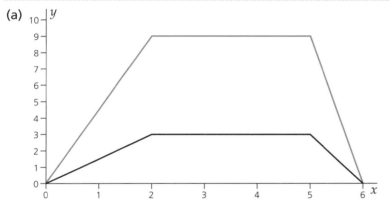

The graph of $y = 3f(x)$ is obtained by applying a stretch with scale factor 3 parallel to the y-axis.

The graph shows the new graph and the original.

(b)
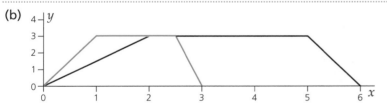

The graph of $y = f(2x)$ is found by applying a stretch with a scale factor of $\frac{1}{2}$ parallel to the x-axis.

EXAMPLE 2

- State the two transformations that should be applied to the graph of $y = f(x)$ to obtain the graph of $y = 4f(x - 6)$.

SOLUTION

First apply a translation of 6 units parallel to the x-axis in the positive direction.	This would give $y = f(x - 6)$.
Apply a stretch with scale factor 4 parallel to the y-axis.	This would then multiply the equation by 4 to give $y = 4f(x - 6)$.

COMBINATIONS OF TRANSFORMATIONS II

KEY POINTS AND DEFINITIONS

- If a graph has equation $y = f(x)$, then:
  - $y = -f(x)$ is a reflection in the x-axis;
  - $y = f(-x)$ is a reflection in the y-axis.

EXAMPLE 1

- The graph of $y = f(x)$ is shown in the diagram.

  Sketch the graphs with equation:

  (a) $y = 2f(x + 2)$ **(b)** $y = 3f(2x)$.

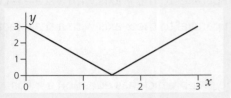

SOLUTION

(a)

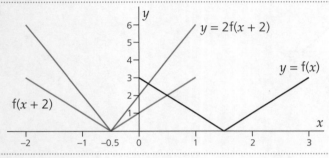

Moving the graph two units to the left gives $y = f(x + 2)$.

A stretch parallel to the y-axis with scale factor 2 can then be applied to give $y = 2f(x + 2)$.

(b)

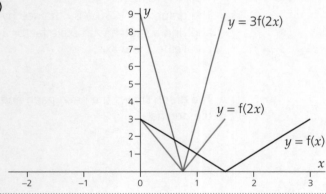

First apply a stretch parallel to the x-axis with scale factor $\frac{1}{2}$ to obtain $y = f(2x)$.

Then apply a stretch parallel to the y-axis with scale factor 3 to obtain $y = 3f(2x)$.

EXAMPLE 2

- The graph shows $y = f(x)$.

  Sketch the graphs of $y = -f(x)$ and $y = f(-x)$.

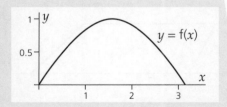

SOLUTION

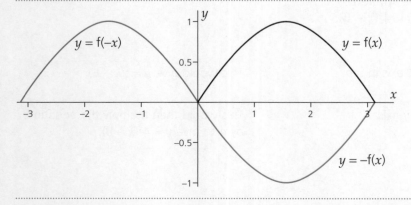

$y = -f(x)$ is obtained by a reflection in the x-axis.

$y = f(-x)$ is obtained by a reflection in the y-axis.

INVERSE TRIGONOMETRIC FUNCTIONS I

KEY POINTS AND DEFINITIONS

- These functions written as $\cos^{-1} x$, $\sin^{-1} x$ and $\tan^{-1} x$ are the inverses of the corresponding trigonometric functions. Because of the periodic nature of the trigonometric functions, the domains of the inverse trigonometric functions are restricted.

  - For $\sin^{-1} x$, the domain is $-1 \leq x \leq 1$ and the range is $-90° \leq x \leq 90°$ or $-\frac{\pi}{2} \leq x \leq \frac{\pi}{2}$.
  - For $\cos^{-1} x$, the domain is $-1 \leq x \leq 1$ and the range is $0 \leq x \leq 180°$ or $0 \leq x \leq \pi$.
  - For $\tan^{-1} x$, the domain is the set of all real numbers and the range is $-90° \leq x \leq 90°$ or $-\frac{\pi}{2} \leq x \leq \frac{\pi}{2}$.

- As with any inverse function, the graphs of the inverse trigonometric functions can be obtained by reflecting the graph of the original trigonometric function in the line $y = x$.

- Remember that $\sin^{-1} x \neq \dfrac{1}{\sin x}$ etc.

EXAMPLE 1

- Sketch the graph of $y = \sin^{-1} x$.

SOLUTION

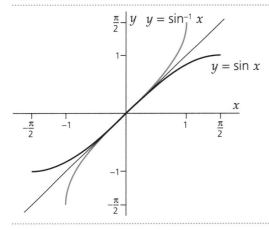

To obtain the graph of $y = \sin^{-1} x$, reflect the graph of $y = \sin x$ in the line $y = x$.

EXAMPLE 2

- Sketch the graph of $y = \cos^{-1} x$.

SOLUTION

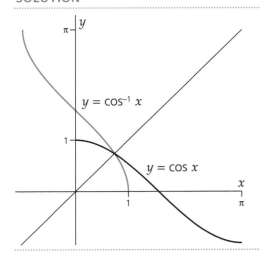

To obtain the graph of $y = \cos^{-1} x$, reflect the graph of $y = \cos x$ in the line $y = x$.

AQA C3

Edexcel C3

OCR C3

OCR(MEI) C3

WJEC C3

INVERSE TRIGONOMETRIC FUNCTIONS II

KEY POINTS AND DEFINITIONS

- Remember the domains and ranges of the inverse trigonometric functions.

EXAMPLE 1

- Sketch the graph of $y = \tan^{-1} x$.

SOLUTION

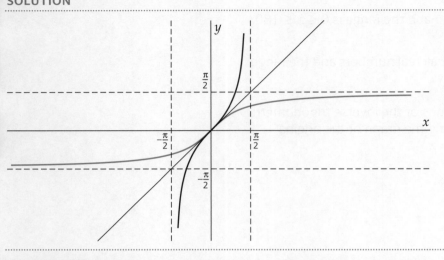

To obtain the graph of $y = \tan^{-1} x$, reflect the graph of $y = \tan x$ in the line $y = x$.

$y = \tan x$ has vertical asymptotes and $y = \tan^{-1} x$ has horizontal asymptotes as shown in the graph.

EXAMPLE 2

- A function, h(x), is defined as $h(x) = \sin^{-1} x + \cos^{-1} x$.

    (a) State the domain of the function.

    (b) Find h(-1), h(0) and h(1).

    (c) By sketching the graphs of $y = \sin^{-1} x$, $y = \cos^{-1} x$ and $y = h(x)$ on the same axes, find the range of h(x).

SOLUTION

(a) $-1 \le x \le 1$	Both $\sin^{-1} x$ and $\cos^{-1} x$ have the same domain of $-1 \le x \le 1$.
(b) $h(-1) = \sin^{-1}(-1) + \cos^{-1}(-1) = -\dfrac{\pi}{2} + \pi = \dfrac{\pi}{2}$	Substitute $x = -1$.
$h(0) = \sin^{-1}(0) + \cos^{-1}(0) = 0 + \dfrac{\pi}{2} = \dfrac{\pi}{2}$	Substitute $x = 0$.
$h(1) = \sin^{-1}(1) + \cos^{-1}(1) = \dfrac{\pi}{2} + 0 = \dfrac{\pi}{2}$	Substitute $x = 1$.
(c) 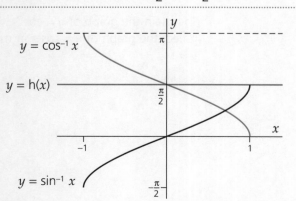	Reflecting each curve in the line $y = \dfrac{\pi}{4}$ would give the other curve. So adding the functions together will always give the same value of $\dfrac{\pi}{2}$.
$h(x) = \dfrac{\pi}{2}$	State the range.

RECIPROCAL TRIGONOMETRIC FUNCTIONS

KEY POINTS AND DEFINITIONS

- The three functions, secant, cosecant and cotangent, are the reciprocals of the three standard trigonometric functions, cosine, sine and tangent.

EXAMPLE 1

- Find the values of:

  (a) $\cot 45°$ (b) $\sec 180°$ (c) $\operatorname{cosec} 30°$.

SOLUTION

(a) $\cot 45° = \dfrac{1}{\tan 45°} = 1$ | Use the definition and the fact that $\tan 45° = 1$.

(b) $\sec 180° = \dfrac{1}{\cos 180°} = \dfrac{1}{-1} = -1$ | Use the definition and the fact that $\cos 180° = -1$.

(c) $\operatorname{cosec} 30° = \dfrac{1}{\sin 30°} = \dfrac{1}{0.5} = 2$ | Use the definition and the fact that $\sin 30° = \dfrac{1}{2} = 0.5$.

EXAMPLE 2

- (a) Show that $\tan^2 x + 1 = \sec^2 x$ and that $1 + \cot^2 x = \operatorname{cosec}^2 x$.

  (b) Hence show that $\dfrac{\tan^2 x + 1}{\cot^2 x + 1} = \tan^2 x$.

SOLUTION

(a) $\sin^2 x + \cos^2 x = 1$ | Start with this identity.

$\dfrac{\sin^2 x}{\cos^2 x} + \dfrac{\cos^2 x}{\cos^2 x} = \dfrac{1}{\cos^2 x}$ | Divide each term by $\cos^2 x$ to obtain the result.

$\dfrac{\sin^2 x}{\cos^2 x} + 1 = \dfrac{1}{\cos^2 x}$

$\tan^2 x + 1 = \sec^2 x$

$\sin^2 x + \cos^2 x = 1$ | Start in the same way.

$\dfrac{\sin^2 x}{\sin^2 x} + \dfrac{\cos^2 x}{\sin^2 x} = \dfrac{1}{\sin^2 x}$ | Divide each term by $\sin^2 x$ to obtain the result.

$1 + \dfrac{\cos^2 x}{\sin^2 x} = \dfrac{1}{\sin^2 x}$

$1 + \cot^2 x = \operatorname{cosec}^2 x$

(b) $\dfrac{\tan^2 x + 1}{\cot^2 x + 1} = \dfrac{\sec^2 x}{\operatorname{cosec}^2 x}$ | Use the two results in (a) as a starting point and remember that $\dfrac{1}{\operatorname{cosec} x} = \sin x$.

$= \dfrac{1}{\cos^2 x} \times \sin^2 x$

$= \tan^2 x$

GRAPHS OF THE RECIPROCAL TRIGONOMETRIC FUNCTIONS

KEY POINTS AND DEFINITIONS

- The graphs of the reciprocal trigonometric functions can be drawn from the standard trigonometric functions.

EXAMPLE 1

- Draw the graph of $y = \cos x$ and $y = \sec x$.

SOLUTION

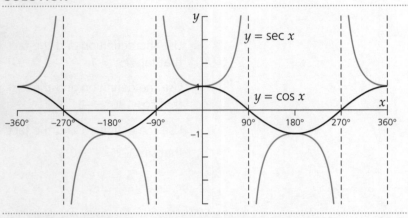

The graph of $y = \sec x$ has vertical asymptotes $x = -270$, $x = -90$, $x = 90$ and $x = 270$.

EXAMPLE 2

- Draw the graph of $y = \sin x$ and $y = \operatorname{cosec} x$.

SOLUTION

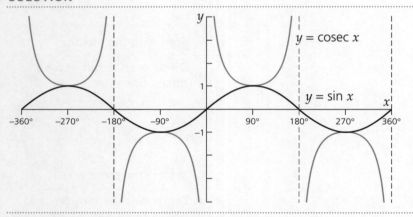

The graph of $y = \operatorname{cosec} x$ has vertical asymptotes $x = -360$, $x = -180$, $x = 0$, $x = 180$ and $x = 360$.

EXAMPLE 3

- Draw the graph of $y = \tan x$ and $y = \cot x$.

SOLUTION

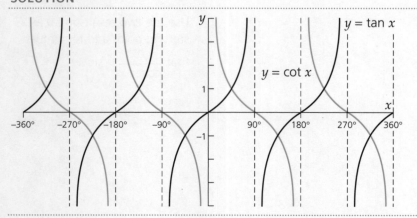

The graph of $y = \tan x$ has vertical asymptotes $x = -270$, $x = -90$, $x = 90$ and $x = 270$.

The graph of $y = \cot x$ has vertical asymptotes $x = -360$, $x = -180$, $x = 0$, $x = 180$ and $x = 360$.

SOLUTION OF EQUATIONS WITH RECIPROCAL TRIGONOMETRIC FUNCTIONS I

KEY POINTS AND DEFINITIONS

- When presented with an equation that contains a reciprocal trigonometric function, convert the equation into one that contains one of the standard trigonometric functions: sin, cos or tan. Then solve this equation in the conventional way.

EXAMPLE 1

- Solve the equation $\sec x = 10$, giving all the solutions in the range $0 \leq x \leq 360°$.

SOLUTION

$\sec x = 10$ $\dfrac{1}{\cos x} = 10$ $\cos x = \dfrac{1}{10} = 0.1$	Use $\sec x = \dfrac{1}{\cos x}$ to express the equation in terms of $\cos x$.
$x = 84.3°$	Find one solution from the calculator.
or $x = 360 - 84.3 = 275.7°$	Find the second solution.

EXAMPLE 2

- Solve the equation $\operatorname{cosec}(2x) = 2$, giving all the solutions in the range $0 \leq x \leq 360°$.

SOLUTION

$\operatorname{cosec}(2x) = 2$ $\dfrac{1}{\sin(2x)} = 2$ $\sin(2x) = \dfrac{1}{2}$	Rearrange the equation using $\operatorname{cosec} x = \dfrac{1}{\sin x}$.
$2x = 30$ or $2x = 180 - 30 = 150$ or $2x = 360 + 30 = 390$ or $2x = 360 + 150 = 510$	Find four values for $2x$ in the range $0 \leq x \leq 720°$.
$x = \dfrac{30}{2} = 15°$ or $x = \dfrac{150}{2} = 75°$ or $x = \dfrac{390}{2} = 195°$ or $x = \dfrac{510}{2} = 255°$	Divide each value by 2 to find the four solutions.

EXAMPLE 3

- Solve the equation $\cot x = \cos x$, giving all the solutions in the range $0 \leq x \leq 360°$.

SOLUTION

$\cot x = \cos x$ $\dfrac{\cos x}{\sin x} = \cos x$	Use $\cot x = \dfrac{\cos x}{\sin x}$.
$\cos x = \cos x \sin x$ $\cos x - \cos x \sin x = 0$ $\cos x(1 - \sin x) = 0$ $\cos x = 0$ or $\sin x = 1$	Multiply by $\cos x$ and then factorise to find values for $\cos x$ and $\sin x$.
$\cos x = 0 \Rightarrow x = 90°$ or $x = 270°$ $\sin x = 1 \Rightarrow x = 90°$	Find the corresponding values of x.
$x = 90°$ or $x = 270°$	State the final solution.

SOLUTION OF EQUATIONS WITH RECIPROCAL TRIGONOMETRIC FUNCTIONS II

KEY POINTS AND DEFINITIONS

- When presented with an equation that contains a reciprocal trigonometric function that has been squared, use one of the identities listed opposite. Then convert the equation into one that contains one of the standard trigonometric functions: sin, cos or tan. Solve this equation in the conventional way.

> **MUST REMEMBER ...**
> $\tan^2 x + 1 = \sec^2 x$
> $1 + \cot^2 x = \csc^2 x$

EXAMPLE 1

- Solve the equation $\cot^2 x + \csc x = 29$, giving all the solutions in the range $0 \le x \le 360°$.

SOLUTION

$\cot^2 x + \csc x = 29$ $\csc^2 x - 1 + \csc x = 29$	Use $\cot^2 x = \csc^2 x - 1$ to replace the $\cot^2 x$ term.
$\csc^2 x + \csc x - 30 = 0$ $(\csc x + 6)(\csc x - 5) = 0$ $\csc x = -6$ or $\csc x = 5$	Rearrange the equation and solve to find two values for $\csc x$.
$\dfrac{1}{\sin x} = -6$ or $\dfrac{1}{\sin x} = 5$ $\sin x = -\dfrac{1}{6}$ or $\sin x = \dfrac{1}{5}$	Use $\csc x = \dfrac{1}{\sin x}$ to find two values for $\sin x$.
$x = -9.6$ (from calculator) $x = 180 - (-9.6) = 189.6°$ $x = 360 - 9.6 = 350.4°$ or $x = 11.5°$ $x = 180 - 11.5 = 168.5°$	Find the values of x, in the range $0 \le x \le 360°$, that satisfy these equations.

EXAMPLE 2

- Solve the equation $\sec x + \tan^2 x + 1 = 0$, giving all the solutions in the range $0 \le x \le 360°$.

SOLUTION

$\sec x + \sec^2 x - 1 + 1 = 0$ $\sec x + \sec^2 x = 0$	Use $\tan^2 x = \sec^2 x - 1$ to replace the $\tan^2 x$ term.
$\sec x(1 + \sec x) = 0$ $\sec x = 0$ or $\sec x = -1$	Simplify the equation and obtain two values for $\sec x$. It is not possible for $\sec x$ to be equal to zero and so there is only one value of $\sec x$ to consider.
$\dfrac{1}{\cos x} = -1$ $\cos x = -1$	Use $\sec x = \dfrac{1}{\cos x}$ to find values for $\cos x$.
$x = 180°$	For this value of $\cos x$, there is only one value of x in the range $0 \le x \le 360°$.

THE EXPONENTIAL FUNCTION I

KEY POINTS AND DEFINITIONS

- Functions of the form $y = a^x$ are called exponential functions; a is a constant called the base.

- As x gets larger, a^x gets larger (at an increasing rate) so that $y \to \infty$ as $x \to \infty$.

- As x gets smaller, a^x gets smaller (at an decreasing rate) so that $y \to 0$ as $x \to -\infty$.

EXAMPLE 1

- On the same axes, sketch graphs of:

  (a) $y = 4^x$ **(b)** $y = 4^{-x}$ **(c)** $y = 4^{\frac{1}{2} - x}$.

  For parts **(b)** and **(c)**, describe the geometrical transformations which map the graph of $y = 4^x$ onto the curve.

SOLUTION

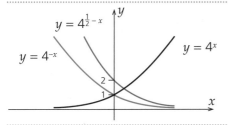

Must remember that $4^0 = 1$ and that, as $x \to -\infty$, $4^x \to 0$.

The graph of $y = 4^{-x}$ is a reflection of the graph of $y = 4^x$ in the y-axis.

The graph of $y = 4^{\frac{1}{2} - x}$ is translation of $\frac{1}{2}$ (to the right) parallel to the x-axis followed by a reflection of the graph in the y-axis.

In this case, split the transformation into two parts.

EXAMPLE 2

- Given that $f(x) = 3^x$ show that each of these relations is true.

  $f(0) = 1; \; f(x + y) = f(x) \times f(y); \; \dfrac{f(x)}{f(y)} = f(x - y); \; (f(x))^n = f(nx)$

SOLUTION

$f(0) = 3^0 = 1$	
$f(x + y) = 3^{x + y}$ $\quad = 3^x \times 3^y$ $\quad = f(x) \times f(y)$	To solve this problem, use the rules for manipulating indices: $a^m \times a^n = a^{m + n}$.
$\dfrac{f(x)}{f(y)} = \dfrac{3^x}{3^y}$ $\quad = 3^{x - y}$ $\quad = f(x - y)$	$a^m \div a^n = a^{m - n}$.
$(f(x))^n = (3^x)^n$ $\quad = (3)^{nx}$ $\quad = f(nx)$	$(a^m)^n = a^{mn}$.

AQA C2

Edexcel C2

OCR C2

OCR(MEI) C2

WJEC C2

THE EXPONENTIAL FUNCTION II

KEY POINTS AND DEFINITIONS

- The 'natural' exponential function e^x has as its base one of the basic constants of mathematics, $e = 2.7182818459$ (to 10 d.p.). e is an irrational number.

- The exponential function, e^x, is defined in two equivalent ways:

$$e^x = \lim_{n \to \infty} \left(1 + \frac{x}{n}\right)^n \quad \text{or} \quad e^x = 1 + x + \frac{x^2}{2!} + \frac{x^3}{3!} + \frac{x^4}{4!} + \dots$$

EXAMPLE 1

- Show that as n gets larger, the value of $\left(1 + \frac{1}{n}\right)^n$ tends towards the limit $e = 2.71828$ (to 5 d.p.).

SOLUTION

n	$\left(1 + \frac{1}{n}\right)^n$
1	2
10	2.59374246
100	2.704813829
1000	2.716923932
10000	2.718145927
100000	2.718268237
1000000	2.718280469

In problems such as these, choose n to be an increasing sequence of integers. Here, powers of 10 have been chosen, but other choices are possible.

This value is correct to five decimal places!

EXAMPLE 2

- **(a)** Sketch a graph of the curve with equation $y = e^{-x} - 1$.

  (b) On the same axes, sketch the graph of $y = \frac{1}{2}|x - 1|$. Show the coordinates of the points where the two graphs meet the axis.

  (c) The x-coordinate of the point of intersection of the two graphs is a. Show that $-1 < a < 0$.

SOLUTION

(a) (b)

The graphs show that the two curves intersect.

(c) Let $f(x) = (e^{-x} - 1) - \frac{1}{2}|x - 1|$

$f(-1) = e^1 - 1 - \frac{1}{2}|-1 - 1| = e^1 - 2 = 0.718$

$f(0) = e^0 - 1 - \frac{1}{2}|0 - 1| = e^0 - 1\frac{1}{2} = -\frac{1}{2}$

Since $f(x)$ changes sign and is a continuous function, $f(x) = 0$ between -1 and 0. Hence the two graphs intersection at a point $x = a$ where $-1 < a < 0$.

To test the inequality for the x-coordinate of the point of intersection, a, find the y-values on each side of $f(x)$ showing that the function $f(x)$ changes sign. Must remember that $f(x)$ must be continuous.

LOGARITHMS

KEY POINTS AND DEFINITIONS

- Logarithms are defined by their relationship to exponential functions.
- If $y = a^x$ then $x = \log_a y$ is called the logarithm of y to base a. Exponential and logarithm functions to the same base are inverse functions.
- If $a = 10$, then $\log_{10} x$ is written $\log x$, i.e. the base 10 is not included; these are called common logarithms.
- If $a = e$, then $\log_e x$ is written $\ln x$; these are called natural logarithms.

EXAMPLE 1

- Given that $y = \log_a x$ $(x > 0)$ where a is a positive constant:

  (a) write x in terms of a and y and deduce that $\log x = y\log a$;

  (b) hence solve the equation $3.72 = \log_5 x$.

SOLUTION

(a) $y = \log_a x \Rightarrow x = a^y$ $\log x = \log a^y = y\log a$	Use the basic relation between exponentials and logarithms.
(b) $3.72 = \log_5 x$ $\log x = 3.72\log 5 = 2.6002$ $x = 10^{2.6002} = 398.26$	Must remember that log means $\log_{10}$.

EXAMPLE 2

- Find the value of x for which $\log_3(x^2 + 5x + 4) - \log_3(x^2 + x) = 2$.

SOLUTION

$\log_3(x^2 + 5x + 4) - \log_3(x^2 + x) = 2$ $\log_3 \dfrac{(x^2 + 5x + 4)}{(x^2 + x)} = \log_3 \dfrac{(x + 4)(x + 1)}{x(x + 1)} = \log_3 \dfrac{(x + 4)}{x} = 2$ $\dfrac{(x + 4)}{x} = 3^2 = 9$ $x + 4 = 9x$ $x = \dfrac{1}{2}$	Use $\log_a x - \log_a y = \log_a \dfrac{x}{y}$. Factorise and simplify.

EXAMPLE 3

- Solve the equation $10^{2x} + 10^x - 2 = 0$

SOLUTION

$10^{2x} + 10^x - 2 = 0$ $(10^x + 2)(10^x - 1) = 0$ $10^x = -2$ or $10^x = 1$ Since $10^x > 0$, reject $10^x = -2$. $10^x = 1 \Rightarrow x = 0$	This is a quadratic equation in 10^x which can be factorised.

THE RELATIONSHIP BETWEEN e^x AND ln x

KEY POINTS AND DEFINITIONS

- The natural logarithm function, $\ln x$, is the inverse of e^x, that is,

  if $y = e^x$ then $x = \ln y$.

EXAMPLE 1

- Express each of these as a single logarithm.

  (a) $3\ln 10 - 2\ln 5$ (b) $\frac{1}{3}\ln 125 + \frac{1}{2}\ln 25$

SOLUTION

(a) $3\ln 10 - 2\ln 5 = \ln (10^3) - \ln (5^2) = \ln \frac{1000}{25} = \ln 40$	Use the laws of logarithms.
(b) $\frac{1}{3}\ln 125 + \frac{1}{2}\ln 25 = \ln 125^{\frac{1}{3}} + \ln 25^{\frac{1}{2}} = \ln 5 + \ln 5 = \ln 25$	

EXAMPLE 2

- Solve the equations.

  (a) $e^x = 5$ (b) $3 - 4\ln x = 0$ (c) $3\ln x^3 + 4\ln x = 9$ (d) $e^{2x} - 7e^x + 12 = 0$

SOLUTION

(a) $e^x = 5 \Rightarrow x = \ln 5 = 1.6094$ (4 d.p.)	Take logs of both sides.
(b) $3 - 4\ln x = 0$ $\ln x = \frac{3}{4}$ $x = e^{\frac{3}{4}} = 2.1170$	$\ln x = y \Rightarrow x = e^y$.
(c) $3\ln x^3 + 4\ln x = 9$ $9\ln x + 4\ln x = 9$ $13\ln x = 9$ $\ln x = \frac{9}{13} \Rightarrow x = e^{\frac{9}{13}} = 1.9983$	Use $\ln x^n = n\ln x$.
(d) $e^{2x} - 7e^x + 12 = 0$ $(e^x - 4)(e^x - 3) = 0$ $e^x = 4$ or $e^x = 3$ $x = \ln 4 = 1.3863$ or $x = \ln 3 = 1.0986$	This is a quadratic equation in e^x.

EXAMPLE 3

- Given that $\ln a = 5$ and $\ln b = 7$, express the following as simple exponentials.

  (a) $a \times b$ (b) $a + b$ (c) $\frac{a}{b}$

SOLUTION

(a) $\ln a = 5 \Rightarrow a = e^5$ and $\ln b = 7 \Rightarrow b = e^7$ $a \times b = e^5 \times e^7 = e^{12}$	Also, $\ln (a \times b) = \ln a + \ln b = 12$ so $a \times b = e^{12}$.
(b) $a + b = e^5 + e^7 = e^5(1 + e^2)$	
(c) $\frac{a}{b} = \frac{e^5}{e^7} = e^{-2}$	Also, $\ln \frac{a}{b} = \ln a - \ln b = -2$ so $\frac{a}{b} = e^{-2}$.

DIFFERENTIATION OF e^x

KEY POINTS AND DEFINITIONS

- Must remember that $\frac{d}{dx}e^{kx} = ke^{kx}$.

EXAMPLE 1

- The level of radioactivity of a substance is given by $R = 60e^{-0.2t}$. Find the rate at which the level of radioactivity is decreasing when:

    (a) $t = 20$ (b) $R = 30$.

SOLUTION

$R = 60e^{-0.2t}$ $\frac{dR}{dt} = 60 \times (-0.2)e^{-0.2t} = -12e^{-0.2t}$	The rate of change is given by $\frac{dR}{dt}$ so find this first.
(a) When $t = 20$, $\frac{dR}{dt} = -12e^{-0.2 \times 20} = -12e^{-4} = -0.2198$ (to 4 d.p.)	Substitute $t = 20$ to find the required rate of change.
(b) When $R = 30$, $30 = 60e^{-0.2t} \Rightarrow e^{-0.2t} = \frac{1}{2}$ $\frac{dR}{dt} = -12e^{-0.2t} = -12 \times \frac{1}{2} = -6$	It is not necessary to find t.

EXAMPLE 2

- If $f(x) = e^{3x} - 7x$, find the range of values of x for which $f(x)$ is a decreasing function.

SOLUTION

$f(x) = e^{3x} - 7x$ $f'(x) = 3e^{3x} - 7$	
For a decreasing function, $f'(x) < 0 \Rightarrow 3e^{3x} - 7 < 0$ $e^{3x} < \frac{7}{3}$	For a decreasing function, $f'(x) < 0$ is needed.
$x < \frac{1}{3}\ln\frac{7}{3}$	Work in exact form, when possible.

EXAMPLE 3

- The curve C has equation $y = 3e^{2x} - x + 2$.

    (a) Find the coordinates of the local minimum.

    (b) Find the equation of the tangent to C at the point (0, 5).

SOLUTION

$y = 3e^{2x} - x + 2 \Rightarrow \frac{dy}{dx} = 6e^{2x} - 1$	
(a) $\frac{dy}{dx} = 0 \Rightarrow 6e^{2x} - 1 = 0$	At a stationary point $\frac{dy}{dx} = 0$.
$e^{2x} = \frac{1}{6} \Rightarrow x = \frac{1}{2}\ln\frac{1}{6} = -\frac{1}{2}\ln 6$	
$\frac{d^2y}{dx^2} = 12e^{2x} = 12 \times \frac{1}{6} = 2 > 0$ The stationary point is a local minimum.	At a local minimum $\frac{d^2y}{dx^2} > 0$.
Coordinates are $(-\frac{1}{2}\ln 6, \frac{1}{2} + \frac{1}{2}\ln 6 + 2) = (-0.8959, 3.3959)$	
(b) At $x = 0$, $\frac{dy}{dx} = 5$	The gradient of the tangent at (0, 5) is
The equation of the tangent is $y = 5x + c$ When $x = 0$, $y = 5 \Rightarrow c = 5$ The equation of the tangent is $y = 5x + 5$	the value of $\frac{dy}{dx}$ at $x = 0$.

DIFFERENTIATION OF ln x

KEY POINTS AND DEFINITIONS

- Must remember that $\frac{d}{dx}$ ln $(kx) = \frac{1}{x}$.

EXAMPLE 1

- Find and classify the stationary points of the function
  f(x) = x^2 − 8ln 0.5x, $x > 0$.

SOLUTION

f(x) = x^2 − 8ln 0.5x f'(x) = $2x - \frac{8}{x}$	
f'(x) = 0 $\Rightarrow 2x - \frac{8}{x} = 0$ $2x^2 - 8 = 0 \Rightarrow x = \pm 2$	At a stationary point, f'(x) = 0.
Since $x > 0$, stationary point is at $x = 2$: f(2) = 2^2 − 8ln 0.5 × 2 = 4	Must remember that ln 1 = 0.
f''(x) = $2 + \frac{8}{x^2}$ At $x = 2$, f''(2) = $2 + \frac{8}{2^2} = 4 > 0 \Rightarrow$ stationary point at (2, 4) is a local minimum	Use the second derivative test to explore the nature of the stationary point.

EXAMPLE 2

- The curve C has equation $y = 5\ln x + \frac{2}{x}$ for $x > 0$.

  The point A on the curve has coordinates (1, 2).

  (a) Find the equation for the normal to C at A.

  (b) The normal to C at A meets the curve again at the point B. Show that the x-coordinate of B lies between 0.18 and 0.19.

SOLUTION

$y = 5\ln x + \frac{2}{x}$ $\frac{dy}{dx} = \frac{5}{x} - \frac{2}{x^2}$	Find $\frac{dy}{dx}$ to obtain the gradient of the curve.
(a) When $x = 1$, $\frac{dy}{dx} = 5 - 2 = 3$ The gradient of the normal is $-\frac{1}{3}$ The equation of the normal is $y = -\frac{1}{3}x + c$ When $x = 1$, $y = 2 \Rightarrow c = 2 + \frac{1}{3} = \frac{7}{3}$ The equation of the normal is $y = -\frac{1}{3}x + \frac{7}{3}$	The gradient of the normal to C at A is $-\frac{1}{\frac{dy}{dx}}$ at $x = 1$.
(b) The normal meets the curve again when $-\frac{1}{3}x + \frac{7}{3} = 5\ln x + \frac{2}{x}$ i.e. when g(x) = $5\ln x + \frac{2}{x} + \frac{1}{3}x - \frac{7}{3} = 0$	The normal meets the curve where the y-coordinates of each equation are equal.
At $x = 0.18$, g(0.18) = +0.264 At $x = 0.19$, g(0.19) = −0.047	Find the values of g(x) at $x = 0.18$ and 0.19.
The function g(x) is continuous and changes sign between $x = 0.18$ and $x = 0.19$. So the x-coordinate of B lies between 0.18 and 0.19.	

DIFFERENTIATION OF TRIGONOMETRIC FUNCTIONS I

KEY POINTS AND DEFINITIONS

- Must remember that it is important to set the calculator to radian mode when working with calculus and trigonometric functions.

MUST REMEMBER ...

$$\frac{d}{dx} \sin kx = k\cos kx$$

$$\frac{d}{dx} \cos kx = -k\sin kx$$

$$\frac{d}{dx} \tan kx = k\sec^2 kx$$

EXAMPLE 1

- Differentiate the following with respect to x.

(a) $3\sin x + 4\cos 2x$ (b) $4 \tan \frac{1}{2}x - 6\sin \frac{3}{4}x$

SOLUTION

(a) $y = 3\sin x + 4\cos 2x$

$\frac{dy}{dx} = 3\cos x + 4(-2\sin 2x) = 3\cos x - 8\sin 2x$

Be careful with cosine – must remember the change of sign!

(b) $y = 4 \tan \frac{1}{2}x - 6\sin \frac{3}{4}x$

$\frac{dy}{dx} = 4(\frac{1}{2}\sec^2 \frac{1}{2}x) - 6(\frac{3}{4}\cos \frac{3}{4}x) = 2\sec^2 \frac{1}{2}x - \frac{9}{2}\cos \frac{3}{4}x$

EXAMPLE 2

- Find the stationary points of the function $y = x - \sin 2x$ in the domain $0 \leq x \leq \neq$ and distinguish between them. Give a rough sketch of the graph of the function.

SOLUTION

$y = x - \sin 2x$

$\frac{dy}{dx} = 1 - 2\cos 2x$

At a stationary point, $\frac{dy}{dx} = 0 \Rightarrow 1 - 2\cos 2x = 0$

$\cos 2x = \frac{1}{2}$

$x = \frac{\pi}{6}$ or $x = \frac{5\pi}{6}$

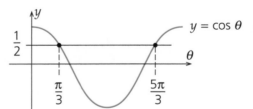

A sketch often helps to solve trigonometric equations.

$\frac{d^2y}{dx^2} = 4\sin 2x$

At $x = \frac{\pi}{6}$, $\frac{d^2y}{dx^2} = 4\sin \frac{2\pi}{6} > 0 \Rightarrow$ stationary point at $\left(\frac{\pi}{6}, \frac{\pi}{6} - \frac{\sqrt{3}}{2}\right)$ is a local minimum

At $x = \frac{5\pi}{6}$, $\frac{d^2y}{dx^2} = 4\sin \frac{10\pi}{6} < 0 \Rightarrow$ stationary point at $\left(\frac{5\pi}{6}, \frac{5\pi}{6} + \frac{\sqrt{3}}{2}\right)$ is a local maximum

State the coordinates of the stationary points.

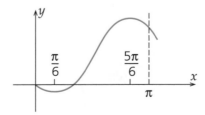

DIFFERENTIATION OF TRIGONOMETRIC FUNCTIONS II

KEY POINTS AND DEFINITIONS

- Several situations can be modelled by trigonometric functions.

EXAMPLE 1

- The temperature $T°C$ of an unheated building is modelled by

$$T = 14 + 2\sin \frac{\pi t}{12} + 5\cos \frac{\pi t}{12} \qquad 0 \le t \le 4$$

where t is the number of hours after noon. Calculate the maximum temperature predicted by the model and the value of t when this occurs.

SOLUTION

$T = 14 + 2\sin \frac{\pi t}{12} + 5\cos \frac{\pi t}{12}$

$\frac{dT}{dt} = 2 \times \frac{\pi}{12}\cos \frac{\pi t}{12} - 5 \times \frac{\pi}{12}\sin \frac{\pi t}{12} = \frac{\pi}{6}\cos \frac{\pi t}{12} - \frac{5\pi}{12}\sin \frac{\pi t}{12}$

$\frac{dT}{dt} = 0$ when $\frac{\pi}{6}\cos \frac{\pi t}{12} - \frac{5\pi}{12}\sin \frac{\pi t}{12} = 0$

| | The maximum temperature occurs when the rate of change of temperature is zero. |

$\tan \frac{\pi t}{12} = \frac{2}{5} \Rightarrow t = 1.45$

$\frac{d^2T}{dt^2} = -2 \times \frac{\pi^2}{12^2}\sin \frac{\pi t}{12} - 5 \times \frac{\pi^2}{12^2}\cos \frac{\pi t}{12} < 0$

Substitute $t = 1.45$ to find the maximum temperature and calculate the time.

The maximum temperature, $T = 19.38°C$ occurs at time 13.27 hours

EXAMPLE 2

- A mass, on the end of a spring, is oscillating in a vertical line between 30 cm and 70 cm above a bench, completing 30 oscillations per minute. The height of the mass, h cm, above the bench after t seconds from being let go from its lowest point can be modelled by a function of the form $h = c - a\cos bt$. Initially, the mass is released at the lowest point of its motion.

(a) Find values for a and c and explain why $b = \pi$.

(b) Sketch a graph of h against t for $0 \le t \le 2$.

(c) Find the velocity of the mass at $t = 1$ and $t = 1.5$.

(d) Find the acceleration of the mass at $t = 1$ and $t = 1.5$.

(e) Comment on your answers to (c) and (d).

SOLUTION

(a) $\frac{2\pi}{b} = 2$, so $b = \pi$

From the model, the period is $\frac{2\pi}{b}$ and from the data, if there are 30 oscillations per minute, the period is 2 seconds.

The amplitude of the oscillation is $\frac{(70 - 30)}{2} = 20 = a$

Use the amplitude to find a.

When $t = 0$, $h = 30$, so $c = 50 \Rightarrow h = 50 - 20\cos \pi t$

Use the initial conditions to find c.

(b)

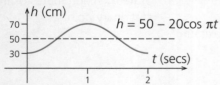

(c) Velocity $= \frac{dh}{dt} = 20\pi\sin \pi t$

Velocity = rate of change of displacement.

When $t = 1$, velocity $= 0$ and when $t = 1.5$, velocity $= -20\pi$

(d) Acceleration $= \frac{d^2h}{dt^2} = 20\pi^2\cos \pi t$

Acceleration = rate of change of velocity.

When $t = 1$, acceleration $= -20\pi^2$ and when $t = 1.5$, acceleration $= 0$

(e) When $t = 1$, the mass is instantaneously at rest at the highest point above the bench; when $t = 1.5$, the mass is moving down with its maximum speed of 20π ms^{-1}

Must remember that h is the distance above the bench.

THE CHAIN RULE

KEY POINTS AND DEFINITIONS

- The chain rule is used to differentiate composite functions, such as $y = \sin x^3$.

EXAMPLE 1

- Differentiate these functions.

  (a) $(3x + 1)^2$ **(b)** $(x^3 + 2)^3$ **(c)** $\ln (4x - 1)^3$ **(d)** $\sin x^3$

SOLUTION

(a) Let $u = 3x + 1$, then $y = u^2$

$\frac{du}{dx} = 3; \frac{dy}{du} = 2u \Rightarrow \frac{dy}{dx} = 2u \times 3 = 6(3x + 1)$

Define the function $u(x)$ and then differentiate each function. Finally apply the chain rule and write the answer in terms of x.
It is possible to write down the answer without defining $u(x)$.

(b) Let $u = x^3 + 2$, then $y = u^3$

$\frac{du}{dx} = 3x^2; \frac{dy}{du} = 3u^2 \Rightarrow \frac{dy}{dx} = 3u^2 \times 3x^2 = 9x^2(x^3 + 2)^2$

The function u often equals the contents of a bracket.

(c) $\ln (4x - 1)^3 = 3\ln (4x - 1)$ so let $u = 4x - 1$, then $y = 3\ln u$

$\frac{du}{dx} = 4; \frac{dy}{du} = \frac{3}{u} \Rightarrow \frac{dy}{dx} = \frac{3}{u} \times 4 = \frac{12}{(4x - 1)}$

Use $\ln a^n = n\ln a$ first.

(d) Let $u = x^3$, then $y = \sin u$

$\frac{du}{dx} = 3x^2; \frac{dy}{du} = \cos u \Rightarrow \frac{dy}{dx} = \cos u \times 3x^2 = 3x^2\cos x^3$

Chose a substitution to give a function that can be easily differentiated.

EXAMPLE 2

- The radius of a circular oil slick is increasing at the rate of 1.5 ms⁻¹.

  (a) Find the rate at which the area of the slick is increasing when its radius is 20 m.

  (b) Find the rate at which the perimeter of the slick is increasing when its radius is 20 m.

SOLUTION

(a) Area of the circular oil slick of radius r is $A = \pi r^2$

$\frac{dA}{dr} = 2\pi r = 40\pi$, when $r = 20$ m

$\frac{dA}{dt} = \frac{dA}{dr} \times \frac{dr}{dt} = 40\pi \times 1.5 = 60\pi$ m²s⁻¹

Area is increasing at a rate of 60π m²s⁻¹

Use the chain rule to find the rate of change of area with respect to time. Must remember that the rate of change of radius is given as 1.5 ms⁻¹.

(b) Perimeter of the circular oil slick of radius r is $C = 2\pi r$

$\frac{dC}{dt} = \frac{dC}{dr} \times \frac{dr}{dt} = 2\pi \times 1.5 = 3\pi$ ms⁻¹

Perimeter is increasing at a rate of 3π ms⁻¹

THE PRODUCT RULE

KEY POINTS AND DEFINITIONS

- The product rule is used to differentiate products of basic functions, such as $y = x^4\cos 2x$.

MUST REMEMBER ...

$$\frac{d(uv)}{dx} = v\frac{du}{dx} + u\frac{dv}{dx}$$

EXAMPLE 1

- Differentiate these functions.

  (a) $(2x + 1)(x^2 - 1)$ **(b)** $x^4\cos 2x$ **(c)** $e^{3x}\ln (2x - 1)$

SOLUTION

(a) $u = 2x + 1$ and $v = x^2 - 1 \Rightarrow \frac{du}{dx} = 2$ and $\frac{dv}{dx} = 2x$

$\frac{d(uv)}{dx} = (x^2 - 1) \times 2 + (2x + 1) \times 2x = 6x^2 + 2x - 2$

| Identify the two functions that make up the product. Then apply the product rule for differentiation. |

(b) $u = x^4$ and $v = \cos 2x \Rightarrow \frac{du}{dx} = 4x^3$ and $\frac{dv}{dx} = -2\sin 2x$

$\frac{d(uv)}{dx} = \cos 2x \times 4x^3 + x^4 \times (-2\sin 2x) = 4x^3\cos 2x - 2x^4\sin 2x$

(c) $u = e^{3x}$ and $v = \ln (2x - 1) \Rightarrow \frac{du}{dx} = 3e^{3x}$ and $\frac{dv}{dx} = \frac{2}{2x - 1}$

$\frac{d(uv)}{dx} = \ln (2x - 1) \times 3e^{3x} + e^{3x} \times \frac{2}{2x - 1} = e^{3x}\left(3\ln(2x - 1) + \frac{2}{2x - 1}\right)$

EXAMPLE 2

- A curve has equation $y = x^3 e^{x^2}$.

  Find the slope of the tangent to the curve at the points $(0, 0)$, $(1, e^1)$ and $(-1, -e^1)$. Is the curve increasing or decreasing at these points? Hence classify the stationary point of the curve at the origin.

SOLUTION

Slope of tangent $= \frac{dy}{dx} = e^{x^2} \times 3x^2 + x^3 \times e^{x^2} \times 2x$	Apply the product rule.
When $x = 0$, $\frac{dy}{dx} = 0 \Rightarrow$ the graph has a stationary point.	Substitute $x = 0$ in the expression for the slope of the tangent.
When $x = 1$, $\frac{dy}{dx} = 3e^1 + 2e^1 = 5e^1 \Rightarrow$ the graph is increasing at $x = 1$ since $\frac{dy}{dx} > 0$	Find the slope when $x = 1$.
When $x = -1$, $\frac{dy}{dx} = 3e^1 + 2e^1 = 5e^1 \Rightarrow$ the graph is increasing at $x = -1$ since $\frac{dy}{dx} > 0$	Find the slope when $x = -1$.
Since the curve is increasing either side of the stationary point and the function is continuous, the stationary point is a point of inflexion.	Classify the stationary point.

THE QUOTIENT RULE

KEY POINTS AND DEFINITIONS

- The quotient rule is used to differentiate a quotient of basic functions, e.g. $y = \dfrac{\cos 2x}{x^4}$.

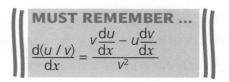

EXAMPLE 1

- Differentiate these functions.

  (a) $\dfrac{(x-2)^3}{x}$ (b) $\dfrac{\cos 2x}{x^4}$

SOLUTION

(a) $u = (x-2)^3$ and $v = x \Rightarrow \dfrac{du}{dx} = 3(x-2)^2$ and $\dfrac{dv}{dx} = 1$

$$\frac{dy}{dx} = \frac{x \times 3(x-2)^2 - 1 \times (x-2)^3}{x^2} = \frac{(x-2)^2(2x+2)}{x^2}$$

> Identify the two functions that make up the quotient. Then apply the quotient rule for differentiation.

(b) $u = \cos 2x$ and $v = x^4 \Rightarrow \dfrac{du}{dx} = -2\sin 2x$ and $\dfrac{dv}{dx} = 4x^3$

$$\frac{dy}{dx} = \frac{x^4 \times (-2\sin 2x) - \cos 2x \times 4x^3}{x^8} = \frac{-2x\sin 2x - 4\cos 2x}{x^5}$$

EXAMPLE 2

- A simple model for the flow rate, $f(v)$ (s^{-1}) of cars along a straight level road is

  $f(v) = \dfrac{v}{4 + 0.7v^2}$, where v is the speed of the cars in ms^{-1}.

  Find the speed of the cars which gives a maximum flow rate. Show that this speed does give a maximum.

SOLUTION

$$\frac{df}{dv} = \frac{(4 + 0.7v^2) \times 1 - v \times 1.4v}{(4 + 0.7v^2)^2} = \frac{4 - 0.7v^2}{(4 + 0.7v^2)^2}$$

Maximum flow when $\dfrac{df}{dv} = 0 \Rightarrow 4 - 0.7v^2 = 0 \Rightarrow v = \sqrt{\dfrac{4}{0.7}} = 2.39 \text{ ms}^{-1}$

> Choose the positive root for the speed of the cars.

$$\frac{d^2 f}{dv^2} = \frac{(4 + 0.7v^2)^2 \times (-1.4v) - (4 - 0.7v^2) \times 2(4 + 0.7v^2) \times 1.4v}{(4 + 0.7v^2)^4}$$

When $v = \sqrt{\dfrac{4}{0.7}}$, $\dfrac{d^2 f}{dv^2} = \dfrac{-1.4 \times \sqrt{\dfrac{4}{0.7}} \times 64 - 0}{8^4} < 0$

> Simply check whether $\dfrac{d^2 f}{dv^2}$ is positive or negative.

$\Rightarrow v = \sqrt{\dfrac{4}{0.7}} = 2.39 \text{ ms}^{-1}$ is a maximum value

> $\dfrac{d^2 f}{dv^2}$ must be negative for a maximum.

DIFFERENTIATING AN INVERSE FUNCTION

KEY POINTS AND DEFINITIONS

- If a function is defined as $x = g(y)$, then the rule for finding $\frac{dy}{dx}$ is
$\frac{dy}{dx} = \frac{1}{\left(\frac{dx}{dy}\right)}$. (This is given in the formula book.)

EXAMPLE 1

- Find $\frac{dy}{dx}$ for these functions.

  (a) $x = y\ln y$ (b) $y = 2^x$ (c) $x = \frac{y}{\ln y}$

SOLUTION

(a) $\frac{dx}{dy} = 1 \times \ln y + y \times \frac{1}{y} = 1 + \ln y$ $\frac{dy}{dx} = \frac{1}{1 + \ln y}$	Use the product rule as a first step.
(b) $y = 2^x \Rightarrow x = \frac{\ln y}{\ln 2}$ $\frac{dx}{dy} = \frac{1}{y\ln 2} \Rightarrow \frac{dy}{dx} = \frac{1}{\left(\frac{1}{y\ln 2}\right)} = y\ln 2 = 2^x\ln 2$	Rearrange to make x the subject.
(c) $\frac{dx}{dy} = \frac{\ln y \times 1 - y \times \frac{1}{y}}{(\ln y)^2} = \frac{\ln y - 1}{(\ln y)^2}$ $\frac{dy}{dx} = \frac{(\ln y)^2}{\ln y - 1}$	Use the quotient rule as a first step.

EXAMPLE 2

- Find the equation of the tangent and the equation of the normal to the curve with equation $x = y^2 - 2y + 1$ at the point $(1, 0)$.

SOLUTION

$x = y^2 - 2y + 1 \Rightarrow \frac{dx}{dy} = 2y - 2 \Rightarrow \frac{dy}{dx} = \frac{1}{2(y - 1)}$ At $y = 0$, $\frac{dy}{dx} = -\frac{1}{2}$	Gradient of a curve is given by $\frac{dy}{dx}$.
Equation of the tangent is $y = -\frac{1}{2}x + c$ When $x = 1$, $y = 0$ so $0 = -\frac{1}{2} + c \Rightarrow c = \frac{1}{2}$	Equation of a straight line is $y = mx + c$ where m is the gradient.
Equation of the tangent is $y = -\frac{1}{2}x + \frac{1}{2}$	
Gradient of the normal $= -\frac{1}{\text{gradient of tangent}} = 2$	
Equation of the normal is $y = 2x + c$	Again, the normal is a straight line.
When $x = 1$, $y = 0$ so $0 = 2 + c \Rightarrow c = -2$	
Equation of the normal is $y = 2x - 2$	

SELECTING A DIFFERENTIATION RULE

KEY POINTS AND DEFINITIONS

- The first step, when differentiating a function, is to identity the form of construction of the function and then apply the appropriate rule.

EXAMPLE

- In the following expressions, find $\dfrac{dy}{dx}$.

  (a) $x = ye^{-y}$

  (b) $y = x\sqrt{x + 2}$

  (c) $y = (2x^3 - 3)^4$

  (d) $y = \dfrac{x}{\sqrt{x + 1}}$

  (e) $y = e^{4x^2 + x - 1}$

SOLUTION

(a) $\dfrac{dx}{dy} = e^{-y} + y(-e^{-y})$ $= e^{-y}(1 - y)$ $= \dfrac{1 - y}{e^y}$ $\dfrac{dy}{dx} = \dfrac{e^y}{1 - y}$	Inverse function rule and the product rule.
(b) $\dfrac{dy}{dx} = \sqrt{x + 2} + x\,\dfrac{1}{2(\sqrt{x + 2})}$ $= \dfrac{3x + 4}{2\sqrt{x + 2}}$	Product rule.
(c) $\dfrac{dy}{dx} = 4(2x^3 - 3)^3 \times 6x^2$ $= 24x^2(2x^3 - 3)^3$	Chain rule for a composite function $u = 2x^3 - 3$, $y = u^4$.
(d) $\dfrac{dy}{dx} = \dfrac{1 \times \sqrt{x + 1} - x \times \dfrac{1}{2\sqrt{x + 1}}}{(x + 1)}$ $= \dfrac{x + 2}{2(x + 1)\sqrt{x + 1}}$	Quotient rule.
(e) $\dfrac{dy}{dx} = e^{4x^2 + x - 1} \times (8x + 1)$	Chain rule for a composite function $u = 4x^2 + x - 1$, $y = e^u$.

AQA C3
Edexcel C3
OCR C3
OCR(MEI) C3
WJEC C3

APPLICATIONS OF THE DIFFERENTIATION RULES

KEY POINTS AND DEFINITIONS

- The differentiation rules can be applied to mathematical models.

EXAMPLE 1

- An object moves along the x-axis so that its position at time $t \geq 0$ is given by

$$x = \frac{4t^2 + t + 4}{t^2 + 1} \text{ metres}$$

(a) Obtain an expression for the velocity of the object and find when the velocity is zero.

(b) What is the greatest distance of the object from the origin?

(c) What is the maximum speed of the object?

SOLUTION

(a) $v = \dfrac{dx}{dt} = \dfrac{(8t + 1) \times (t^2 + 1) - 2t \times (4t^2 + t + 4)}{(t^2 + 1)^2}$ $v = \dfrac{-t^2 + 1}{(t^2 + 1)^2}$	Velocity is the rate of change of position.
$v = 0$ when $-t^2 + 1 = 0 \Rightarrow t = 1$	Choose the positive value as t is time.
(b) Greatest distance from the origin is when $v = 0$ So greatest distance is 4.5 m.	Substitue $t = 0$ into the expression for x.
(c) $\dfrac{dv}{dt} = \dfrac{(-2t) \times (t^2 + 1)^2 - (-t^2 + 1) \times 4t(t^2 + 1)}{(t^2 + 1)^4}$	
$\dfrac{dv}{dt} = \dfrac{2t(t^2 - 3)}{(t^2 + 1)^3} = 0$ when $t = 0$ or $t = \sqrt{3}$	Maximum speed occurs when $\dfrac{dv}{dt} = 0$.
$\dfrac{d^2v}{dt^2} = \dfrac{(6t^2 - 6) \times (t^2 + 1)^3 - (2t^3 - 6t) \times 6t(t^2 + 1)^2}{(t^2 + 1)^6}$	
When $t = 0$, $\dfrac{d^2v}{dt^2} = -6 < 0$, so $t = 0$ gives a maximum speed of 1 ms⁻¹ When $t = \sqrt{3}$, $\dfrac{d^2v}{dt^2} = +\dfrac{3}{16} > 0$: a minimum speed	Use the second derivative test to check that $t = 0$ is a maximum.

EXAMPLE 2

- Wine is spilled onto a carpet forming a circular stain so that the radius, r cm, t seconds after it first appears, is given by

$$r = \frac{1 + 4t}{2 + t}. \text{ Calculate:}$$

(a) the time taken for the radius to double its initial value;

(b) the rate of increase of the radius in cms⁻¹ when $t = 3$;

(c) the value to which r tends as t increases.

SOLUTION

(a) When $t = 0$, $r = \dfrac{1}{2}$ so need value of t when $r = 1$ $r = \dfrac{1 + 4t}{2 + t} = 1$ when $2 + t = 1 + 4t \Rightarrow t = \dfrac{1}{3}$ s	Initial value of radius is found by substituting $t = 0$.
(b) $\dfrac{dr}{dt} = \dfrac{4 \times (2 + t) - 1 \times (1 + 4t)}{(2 + t)^2} = \dfrac{7}{(2 + t)^2}$ When $t = 3$, rate of increase is $\dfrac{7}{25} = 0.28$ cms⁻¹	Rate of increase is the derivative of r.
(c) As $t \to \infty$, $r \to 4$ cm	For large t, r behaves like $\dfrac{4t}{t}$.

INTEGRATION OF e^x

KEY POINTS AND DEFINITIONS

- Must remember that $\int e^{kx} dx = \frac{1}{k} e^{kx} + c$.

EXAMPLE
- Evaluate the following integrals.

    (a) $\int e^{4x} dx$

    (b) $\int_0^1 e^{-x} dx$

    (c) $\int_{-\infty}^0 e^{2x} dx$

    (d) $\int e^{2x+3} dx$

SOLUTION

(a) $\int e^{4x} dx = \frac{1}{4} e^{4x} + c$	Must remember the constant of integration.
(b) $\int_0^1 e^{-x} dx = \left[-e^{-x} \right]_0^1$ $= -e^{-1} - (-e^0)$ $= 1 - e^{-1}$	Use the standard form to integrate e^{-x} and then apply the limits. Be careful with the signs. Must remember that $e^0 = 1$.
(c) $\int_{-\infty}^0 e^{2x} dx = \left[\frac{1}{2} e^{2x} \right]_{-\infty}^0$ $= \frac{1}{2} e^0 - \frac{1}{2} e^{-\infty}$ $= \frac{1}{2}$	Must remember that $e^{-\infty} = 0$.
(d) $\int e^{2x+3} dx = \int e^{2x} \times e^3 dx$ $= e^3 \int e^{2x} dx$ $= e^3 \left(\frac{1}{2} e^{2x} \right) + c$ $= \frac{1}{2} e^{3+2x} + c$	Use $a^{m+n} = a^m \times a^n$.

INTEGRATION OF $\frac{1}{x}$

KEY POINTS AND DEFINITIONS

- Must remember that:

  - $\int \frac{1}{x} dx = \ln |x| + c;$

  - $\int \frac{1}{ax + b} dx = \frac{1}{a} \ln |ax + b| + c.$

EXAMPLE 1

- Evaluate the following integrals.

  (a) $\int \frac{5}{x} dx$

  (b) $\int_0^2 \frac{4}{3x + 1} dx$

  (c) $\int \frac{2x - 5}{x^2} dx$

SOLUTION

(a) $\int \frac{5}{x} dx = 5\ln |x| + c$

(b) $\int_0^2 \frac{4}{3x + 1} dx$

$= \left[\frac{4}{3} \ln |3x + 1| \right]_0^2$

$= \frac{4}{3} \ln 7 - \frac{4}{3} \ln 1$

$= \frac{4}{3} \ln 7$

Must remember that $\ln 1 = 0$.

(c) $\int \frac{2x - 5}{x^2} dx$

$= \int \left(\frac{2x}{x^2} - \frac{5}{x^2} \right) dx$

$= \int \frac{2}{x} dx - \int \frac{5}{x^2} dx$

$= 2\ln |x| + \frac{5}{x} + c$

Split the integrand into two standard forms.

Must be careful with $\int \frac{1}{x^2} dx$. It does not involve logs!

INTEGRATION OF sin x AND cos x

KEY POINTS AND DEFINITIONS

- Must remember that:
  - $\int \sin ax\,dx = -\dfrac{1}{a}\cos ax + c;$
  - $\int \cos ax\,dx = \dfrac{1}{a}\sin ax + c.$

EXAMPLE

- Evaluate the following integrals.

  (a) $\int \sin 3x\,dx$

  (b) $\int \cos 6x\,dx$

  (c) $\int_{-\frac{\pi}{2}}^{\frac{\pi}{2}} (1 + 2\sin 2x)\,dx$

  (d) $\int_{\frac{\pi}{2}}^{\pi} (2\cos x - \sin x)\,dx$

SOLUTION

(a) $\int \sin 3x\,dx = -\dfrac{1}{3}\cos 3x + c$	Must be careful with the signs when integrating sines and cosines.
(b) $\int \cos 6x\,dx = \dfrac{1}{6}\sin 6x + c$	
(c) $\int_{-\frac{\pi}{2}}^{\frac{\pi}{2}} (1 + 2\sin 2x)\,dx$ $= \left[x - \cos 2x \right]_{-\frac{\pi}{2}}^{\frac{\pi}{2}}$ $= \left(\dfrac{\pi}{2} - \cos \pi \right) - \left(\dfrac{-\pi}{2} - \cos(-\pi) \right)$ $= \pi$	$\cos \pi = -1$, $\cos(-\pi) = -1$.
(d) $\int_{\frac{\pi}{2}}^{\pi} (2\cos x - \sin x)\,dx$ $= \left[2\sin x + \cos x \right]_{\frac{\pi}{2}}^{\pi}$ $= (2\sin \pi + \cos \pi) - \left(2\sin \dfrac{\pi}{2} + \cos \dfrac{\pi}{2} \right)$ $= (2 \times 0 - 1) - (2 \times 1 + 0)$ $= -3$	Must try to remember the sine and cosine of simple fractions of π.

AREAS AND INTEGRATION

KEY POINTS AND DEFINITIONS

- For positive functions, the area under a graph between $x = a$ and $x = b$ is found by the definite integral $\int_a^b f(x)dx$.
- For negative functions, the area under a graph between $x = a$ and $x = b$ is found by the definite integral $-\int_a^b f(x)dx$.

EXAMPLE 1

- Find the area of the shaded region.

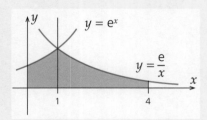

SOLUTION

Area between $x = 0$ and $x = 1$ is $$\int_0^1 e^x dx = \left[e^x \right]_0^1$$ $$= e^1 - e^0$$ $$= e - 1$$	The area can be split into two parts under each function.
	Must remember that $e^0 = 1$.
Area between $x = 1$ and $x = 4$ is $$\int_1^4 \frac{e}{x}dx = \left[e\ln |x| \right]_1^4$$ $$= e\ln 4 - e\ln 1$$ $$= e\ln 4$$	
	Must remember that $\ln 1 = 0$.
Total area of the shaded region is $e + e\ln 4 - 1$	Add the two areas together.

EXAMPLE 2

- The diagram shows the graphs of $y = \sin x$ and $y = \cos x$ in the domain $-\frac{1}{2}\pi \le x \le \pi$.

  Find the area of the region OAC, giving your answer in surd form.

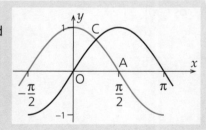

SOLUTION

Point C is $x = \frac{\pi}{4}$ 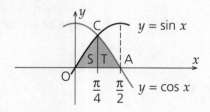	First find the x-value of the point of intersection of the two graphs.
Area OAC $= \int_0^{\frac{\pi}{4}} \sin x\,dx + \int_{\frac{\pi}{4}}^{\frac{\pi}{2}} \cos x\,dx$ $$= \left[-\cos x \right]_0^{\frac{\pi}{4}} + \left[\sin x \right]_{\frac{\pi}{4}}^{\frac{\pi}{2}}$$ $$= (-\cos \frac{\pi}{4} + \cos 0) + (\sin \frac{\pi}{2} - \sin \frac{\pi}{4})$$ $$= -\frac{\sqrt{2}}{2} + 1 + 1 - \frac{\sqrt{2}}{2}$$ $$= 2 - \sqrt{2}$$	Then add together the area under the cos graph (T) and the area under the sin graph (S).
	Simplify the answer.

INTEGRATION BY DIRECT SUBSTITUTION

KEY POINTS AND DEFINITIONS

- Use the method of integration by direct substitution for problems such as $\int x^2 \sin x^3 dx$ by taking $u = x^3$.

- The aim of a substitution is to reduce the integrand to a standard form.

- When using substitutions, must remember to change all the x's into the new variable.

- The substitution to choose usually obvious by inspection of the integrand.

> **MUST REMEMBER ...**
>
> Use $dx = \dfrac{dx}{du} du$ to change dx.

EXAMPLE

- Evaluate the following integrals.

    (a) $\int (x + 5)^4 dx$ (b) $\int x(x^2 + 2)^{\frac{5}{4}} dx$ (c) $\int_0^2 8xe^{4x^2} dx$ (d) $\int \dfrac{3x^2 - 2}{x^3 - 2x + 1} dx$

SOLUTION

(a) For $\int(x + 5)^4 dx$, choose $u = x + 5 \Rightarrow \dfrac{du}{dx} = 1$

$\int(x + 5)^4 dx = \int u^4 du$

$\qquad = \dfrac{u^5}{5} + c$

$\qquad = \dfrac{(x + 5)^5}{5} + c$

Must remember to write the answer in terms of the given variable, x.

(b) For $\int x(x^2 + 2)^{\frac{5}{4}} dx$, choose $u = x^2 + 2 \Rightarrow \dfrac{du}{dx} = 2x$

$\int x(x^2 + 2)^{\frac{5}{4}} dx = \int x \times u^{\frac{5}{4}} \times \dfrac{1}{2x} du = \int \dfrac{1}{2} u^{\frac{5}{4}} du$

$\qquad = \dfrac{1}{2} \times \dfrac{4}{9} u^{\frac{9}{4}} + c$

$\qquad = \dfrac{2}{9}(x^2 + 2)^{\frac{9}{4}} + c$

$\dfrac{dx}{du} = \dfrac{1}{du/dx} = \dfrac{1}{2x}$.

(c) For $\int_0^2 8xe^{4x^2} dx$, choose $u = 4x^2 \Rightarrow \dfrac{du}{dx} = 8x$

$x = 0 \Rightarrow u = 0$ and $x = 2 \Rightarrow u = 16$

Find the new limits.

$\int_0^2 8xe^{4x^2} dx = \int_0^{16} 8xe^{4x^2} \times \dfrac{1}{8x} du = \int_0^{16} e^u du$

Change the x's and write the limits in terms of the new variable.

$\qquad = \left[e^u \right]_0^{16}$

$\qquad = e^{16} - e^0 = e^{16} - 1$

(d) For $\int \dfrac{3x^2 - 2}{x^3 - 2x + 1} dx$, choose $u = x^3 - 2x + 1 \Rightarrow \dfrac{du}{dx} = 3x^2 - 2$

$\int \dfrac{3x^2 - 2}{x^3 - 2x + 1} dx = \int \dfrac{(3x^2 - 2)}{u} \times \dfrac{1}{3x^2 - 2} du = \int \dfrac{1}{u} du$

In each case, the substitution 'works' if all the x's can be removed in the process.

$\qquad = \ln |u| + c$

$\qquad = \ln |x^3 - 2x + 1| + c$

INTEGRATION BY INDIRECT SUBSTITUTION

KEY POINTS AND DEFINITIONS

- Use the method of integration by indirect substitution for problems such as $\int \dfrac{1}{\sqrt{1-x^2}}\,dx$ by taking $x = \sin u$.
- The aim of a substitution is to reduce the integrand to a standard form.
- When using substitutions, must remember to change all the x's into the new variable.
- The substitution to choose usually involves trigonometric functions.

> **MUST REMEMBER ...**
>
> Use $dx = \dfrac{dx}{du}\,du$ to change dx.

EXAMPLE

- Evaluate the following integrals.

  (a) $\displaystyle\int \dfrac{1}{\sqrt{1-x^2}}\,dx$ (b) $\displaystyle\int \dfrac{1}{1+x^2}\,dx$ (c) $\displaystyle\int_0^2 \dfrac{1}{\sqrt{4-x^2}}\,dx$

SOLUTION

(a) For $\displaystyle\int \dfrac{1}{\sqrt{1-x^2}}\,dx$, choose $x = \sin u \Rightarrow \dfrac{dx}{du} = \cos u$

$\displaystyle\int \dfrac{1}{\sqrt{1-x^2}}\,dx = \int \dfrac{1}{\sqrt{1-\sin^2 u}}\cos u\,du = \int \dfrac{1}{\sqrt{\cos^2 u}}\cos u\,du$

$\qquad = \displaystyle\int du = u + c = \sin^{-1} x + c$

Use the identity $\sin^2 u + \cos^2 u = 1$.

(b) For $\displaystyle\int \dfrac{1}{1+x^2}\,dx$, choose $x = \tan u \Rightarrow \dfrac{dx}{du} = \sec^2 u$

$\displaystyle\int \dfrac{1}{1+x^2}\,dx = \int \dfrac{1}{1+\tan^2 u}\sec^2 u\,du = \int du = u + c = \tan^{-1} x + c$

Use the identity $1 + \tan^2 u = \sec^2 u$.

(c) For $\displaystyle\int_0^2 \dfrac{1}{\sqrt{4-x^2}}\,dx$, choose $x = 2\sin u \Rightarrow \dfrac{dx}{du} = 2\cos u$

$x = 0 \Rightarrow u = 0$ and $x = 2 \Rightarrow \sin u = 1 \Rightarrow u = \dfrac{\pi}{2}$

$\displaystyle\int_0^2 \dfrac{1}{\sqrt{4-x^2}}\,dx = \int_0^{\frac{\pi}{2}} \dfrac{1}{\sqrt{4-4\sin^2 u}}2\cos u\,du = \int_0^{\frac{\pi}{2}} du = \dfrac{\pi}{2}$

Change the x's and write the limits in terms of the new variable.

EXAMPLE 2

- Show that the direct substitution $u = 1 - x^2$ does not work to evaluate $\displaystyle\int \dfrac{1}{\sqrt{1-x^2}}\,dx$, but that the indirect substitution $x = \sin u$ can be used.

SOLUTION

With $u = 1 - x^2$, $\dfrac{du}{dx} = -2x$ and

$\displaystyle\int \dfrac{1}{\sqrt{1-x^2}}\,dx = \int \dfrac{1}{\sqrt{u}} \times \dfrac{1}{-2x}\,du = \int \dfrac{1}{\sqrt{u}} \times \dfrac{1}{-2\sqrt{1-u}}\,du$

This direct substitution has not simplified the integrand.

With $x = \sin u$, $\displaystyle\int \dfrac{1}{\sqrt{1-x^2}}\,dx = \int du = \sin^{-1} x + c$

This indirect substitution has worked.

PROVING STANDARD RESULTS USING INTEGRATION BY SUBSTITUTION

KEY POINTS AND DEFINITIONS

- Integration by substitution can be used to prove standard integrals.

EXAMPLE 1

- Prove that $\int (ax + b)^n dx = \dfrac{1}{a(n+1)} (ax+b)^{n+1} + c.$

SOLUTION

For $\int(ax+b)^n dx$, choose $u = ax + b \Rightarrow \dfrac{du}{dx} = a$	Choose a suitable substitution.
$\int(ax+b)^n dx = \int u^n \times \dfrac{1}{a} du = \dfrac{1}{a} \int u^n du$ $= \dfrac{1}{a} \times \dfrac{u^{n+1}}{n+1} + c$ $= \dfrac{1}{a(n+1)} (ax+b)^{n+1} + c$	Must remember to express final answer in terms of x.

EXAMPLE 2

- Prove that $\int \dfrac{1}{ax+b} dx = \dfrac{1}{a} \ln |ax + b| + c.$

SOLUTION

For $\int \dfrac{1}{ax+b} dx$, choose $u = ax + b \Rightarrow \dfrac{du}{dx} = a$	Choose a suitable substitution.
$\int \dfrac{1}{ax+b} dx = \int \dfrac{1}{u} \times \dfrac{1}{a} du$ $= \dfrac{1}{a} \int \dfrac{1}{u} du$ $= \dfrac{1}{a} \ln |u| + c$ $= \dfrac{1}{a} \ln |ax + b| + c$	Must remember that $\int \dfrac{1}{x} dx = \ln |x| + c.$

EXAMPLE 3

- Prove that $\int \tan x \, dx = -\ln |\cos x| + c.$

SOLUTION

$\int \tan x \, dx = \int \dfrac{\sin x}{\cos x} dx$	Express $\tan x$ in terms of $\sin x$ and $\cos x$.
Choose $u = \cos x \Rightarrow \dfrac{du}{dx} = -\sin x$	Choose a suitable substitution.
$\int \dfrac{\sin x}{\cos x} dx = \int \dfrac{\sin x}{u} \times \dfrac{1}{(-\sin x)} du$ $= -\int \dfrac{1}{u} du$ $= -\ln|u| + c$	The expressions involving x cancel.
$\int \tan x \, dx = -\ln |\cos x| + c$	Give the answer in terms of x.

INTEGRATION METHODS AND THE CHAIN AND PRODUCT RULES FOR DIFFERENTIATION

KEY POINTS AND DEFINITIONS

- The link between differentiation and integration often provides a method of approach to integrating functions.

EXAMPLE 1

- Use the chain rule to differentiate $y = \sqrt{(1 + x^3)}$.

  Hence evaluate the integral $\int_0^1 \frac{x^2}{\sqrt{(1 + x^3)}}dx$.

SOLUTION

Choose $u = 1 + x^3 \Rightarrow y = \sqrt{u}$ and $\frac{du}{dx} = 3x^2$	
$\frac{dy}{dx} = \frac{dy}{du} \times \frac{du}{dx} = \frac{1}{2\sqrt{u}} \times 3x^2$ $= \frac{3x^2}{2\sqrt{1 + x^3}}$	This is the chain rule for differentiation.
$\int_0^1 \frac{x^2}{\sqrt{1 + x^3}}dx = \frac{2}{3}\int_0^1 \frac{3x^2}{2\sqrt{1 + x^3}}dx$ $= \left[\frac{2}{3}\sqrt{1 + x^3} \right]_0^1$ $= \frac{2}{3}\sqrt{2} - \frac{2}{3}$	Here the link between integration and differentiation is used.

EXAMPLE 2

- Use the product rule to differentiate $e^x \cos x$ and $e^x \sin x$.

  Hence evaluate the integral $\int e^x \sin x\,dx$.

SOLUTION

$\frac{d}{dx}(e^x \cos x) = e^x \cos x - e^x \sin x \qquad (1)$ $\frac{d}{dx}(e^x \sin x) = e^x \sin x + e^x \cos x \qquad (2)$	In these expressions, the product rule has been used.
To evaluate $\int e^x \sin x\,dx$, consider expression (2) – (1) $2e^x \sin x = \frac{d}{dx}(e^x \sin x - e^x \cos x)$ $\int e^x \sin x\,dx = \int \frac{1}{2}\frac{d}{dx}(e^x \sin x - e^x \cos x)dx$ $= \frac{1}{2}(e^x \sin x - e^x \cos x) + c$	Use the results to obtain an expression for $e^x \sin x$. Must remember the constant of integration.

INTEGRATION BY PARTS I

KEY POINTS AND DEFINITIONS

- The method of integration by parts works for some products of functions.

- It is the integral of a product of functions written as u and $\frac{dv}{dx}$.

- One function, $\frac{dv}{dx}$, is being integrated and the other function, u, is being differentiated.

- Must choose u and $\frac{dv}{dx}$ wisely so that the resulting integral, $\int v\frac{du}{dx}dx$, is easier than the original integral.

- A general rule which works in most cases is to let $u = x^n$.

> **MUST REMEMBER ...**
>
> The formula for integration by parts:
> $$\int u\frac{dv}{dx}dx = uv - \int v\frac{du}{dx}dx$$

EXAMPLE

- Evaluate the following using the method of integration by parts.

  (a) $\int xe^{2x}dx$ (b) $\int_0^{\frac{\pi}{4}} x\sin 2x\,dx$ (c) $\int \ln x\,dx$ (d) $\int_1^2 x^2\ln x\,dx$

SOLUTION

(a) $\int xe^{2x}dx = x \times \frac{e^{2x}}{2} - \int 1 \times \frac{e^{2x}}{2}dx$

$\qquad = \frac{xe^{2x}}{2} - \frac{e^{2x}}{4} + c$

$\qquad\qquad$ $u = x$ and $\frac{dv}{dx} = e^{2x}$.

(b) $\int_0^{\frac{\pi}{4}} x\sin 2x\,dx = \left[-x\frac{\cos 2x}{2}\right]_0^{\frac{\pi}{4}} - \int_0^{\frac{\pi}{4}} -\frac{\cos 2x}{2}dx$

$\qquad = \left[-x\frac{\cos 2x}{2}\right]_0^{\frac{\pi}{4}} + \int_0^{\frac{\pi}{4}} \frac{\cos 2x}{2}dx$

$\qquad = \left[-x\frac{\cos 2x}{2} + \frac{\sin 2x}{4}\right]_0^{\frac{\pi}{4}}$

$\qquad = \left(-\frac{\pi}{4} \times \frac{\cos \frac{\pi}{2}}{2} + \frac{\sin \frac{\pi}{2}}{4}\right) - 0 = \frac{1}{4}$

$\qquad\qquad$ $u = x$ and $\frac{dv}{dx} = \sin 2x$.

In (c) and (d), 'break the rule' and choose $\frac{dv}{dx} = x^n$.

(c) $\qquad \int \ln x\,dx = \ln x \times x - \int \frac{1}{x} \times x\,dx$

$\qquad\qquad = x\ln x - \int dx$

$\qquad\qquad = x\ln x - x + c$

$\qquad\qquad$ Let $\frac{dv}{dx} = 1$ and $u = \ln x$.

(d) $\int x^2 \ln x\,dx = \frac{x^3}{3} \times \ln x - \int \frac{x^3}{3} \times \frac{1}{x}\,dx$

$\qquad\qquad = \frac{x^3}{3}\ln x - \int \frac{x^2}{3}dx$

$\int_1^2 x^2 \ln x\,dx = \left[\frac{x^3}{3}\ln x - \frac{x^3}{9}\right]_1^2$

$\qquad\qquad = \left(\frac{8}{3}\ln 2 - \frac{8}{9}\right) - \left(0 - \frac{1}{9}\right)$

$\qquad\qquad = \frac{8}{3}\ln 2 - \frac{7}{9}$

$\qquad\qquad$ Let $\frac{dv}{dx} = x^2$.

INTEGRATION BY PARTS II

KEY POINTS AND DEFINITIONS

- Often it is necessary to apply the method of integration by parts repeatedly.

EXAMPLE 1

- Evaluate the integral $\int x^2 \cos x\,dx$.

SOLUTION

$$\int x^2 \cos x\,dx = x^2 \sin x - \int 2x \sin x\,dx + c$$

$$\int x \sin x\,dx = x(-\cos x) - \int (-\cos x)\,dx$$ | Now integrate by parts again.

$$= -x\cos x + \sin x$$

$$\int x^2 \cos x\,dx = x^2 \sin x - 2(-x\cos x + \sin x) + c$$ | Put the two parts together.

$$= (x^2 - 2)\sin x + 2x\cos x + c$$

EXAMPLE 2

- Evaluate the integral $\int e^{2x}\sin x\,dx$.

SOLUTION

$$\int e^{2x}\sin x\,dx = e^{2x} \times (-\cos x) - \int 2e^{2x} \times (-\cos x)\,dx$$ | Choose $u = e^{2x}$ and $\dfrac{dv}{dx} = \sin x$.

$$= -e^{2x}\cos x + 2\int e^{2x}\cos x\,dx + c$$

$$\int e^{2x}\cos x\,dx = e^{2x}\sin x - \int 2e^{2x}\sin x\,dx$$ | Now use the method again sticking with $u = e^{2x}$ and $\dfrac{dv}{dx} = \cos x$.

$$= e^{2x}\sin x - 2\int e^{2x}\sin x\,dx$$

$$\int e^{2x}\sin x\,dx = -e^{2x}\cos x + 2e^{2x}\sin x - 4\int e^{2x}\sin x\,dx + c$$ | It appears this is back to the start. However, proceed by adding $4\int e^{2x}\sin x\,dx$ to each side.

$$5\int e^{2x}\sin x\,dx = -e^{2x}\cos x + 2e^{2x}\sin x + c$$

$$\int e^{2x}\sin x\,dx = -\frac{1}{5}e^{2x}\cos x + \frac{2}{5}e^{2x}\sin x + A$$

where $A = \dfrac{c}{5}$ is a constant of integration

EXAMPLE 3

- The integral I_n is defined by $\int x^n e^x\,dx$ for positive integers, n.

  (a) Show that, after one integration, I_n satisfies the sequence $I_n = x^n e^x - nI_{n-1}$.

  (b) Evaluate I_0 directly and hence use the sequence to evaluate $\int x^2 e^x\,dx$.

SOLUTION

(a) $$I_n = \int x^n e^x\,dx = x^n e^x - \int nx^{n-1}e^x\,dx$$ | Choose $u = x^n$ and $\dfrac{dv}{dx} = e^x$.

$$= x^n e^x - nI_{n-1}$$

(b) $$I_0 = \int x^0 e^x\,dx = \int e^x\,dx = e^x$$

$$I_1 = xe^x - I_0 = xe^x - e^x$$ | Use the sequence with $n = 1$.

$$I_2 = x^2 e^x - 2I_1$$ | Use the sequence with $n = 2$.

$$= x^2 e^x - 2(xe^x - e^x) = x^2 e^x - 2xe^x + 2e^x + c$$

So $$\int x^2 e^x\,dx = e^x(x^2 - 2x + 2) + c$$

SELECTING AN INTEGRATION METHOD

KEY POINTS AND DEFINITIONS

- This flowchart gives a systematic way to approach the evaluation of an integral. Other methods are not needed for A2 Mathematics.

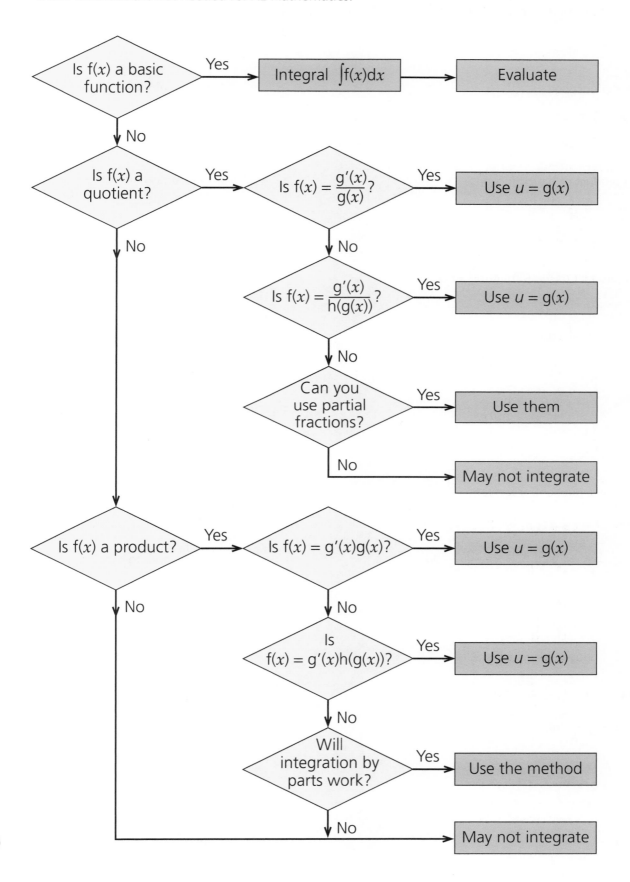

SELECTING AN INTEGRATION METHOD – CONTINUED

EXAMPLE

- Use the flowchart to classify each of the following integrals. Hence evaluate the integral using the appropriate method.

(a) $\int 4x^{\frac{5}{2}}\,dx$ (b) $\int xe^{-2x}dx$ (c) $\int xe^{-3x^2}dx$ (d) $\int_0^1 \frac{3x^2+1}{x^3+x+4}\,dx$ (e) $\int_0^3 \frac{1}{\sqrt{1+t}}\,dt$

SOLUTION

(a) $x^{\frac{5}{2}}$ is a basic function:

$$\int 4x^{\frac{5}{2}}\,dx = 4 \times \frac{2}{7} x^{\frac{7}{2}} + c$$

$$= \frac{8}{7} x^{\frac{7}{2}} + c$$

A standard intregal:

use $\int x^n dx = \frac{x^{n+1}}{n+1} + c$.

(b) xe^{-2x} is a product of basic functions

$$\int xe^{-2x}dx = x \times \frac{e^{-2x}}{(-2)} - \int \frac{e^{-2x}}{(-2)}dx$$

$$= -\frac{1}{2}xe^{-2x} - \frac{1}{4}e^{-2x} + c$$

Use the method of integration by parts.

(c) xe^{-3x^2} is a product of the form $g(u)\frac{du}{dx}$ because,

with $u(x) = -3x^2$ and $\frac{du}{dx} = -6x$:

$$\int xe^{-3x^2}dx = \int xe^{u}\frac{1}{(-6x)}du$$

$$= -\frac{1}{6}\int e^u du$$

$$= -\frac{1}{6}e^u + c$$

$$= -\frac{1}{6}e^{-3x^2} + c$$

Use substitution.

Must remember that $x = \frac{-6x}{-6}$.

(d) $\frac{3x^2+1}{x^3+x+4}$ is a quotient of the form $\frac{\frac{du}{dx}}{u}$

Choose $u = x^3 + x + 4$ with $\frac{du}{dx} = 3x^2 + 1$

$$\int_0^1 \frac{3x^2+1}{x^3+x+4}\,dx = \int_4^6 \frac{(3x^2+1)}{u} \times \frac{1}{(3x^2+1)}du$$

$$= \int_4^6 \frac{1}{u}\,du$$

$$= \Big[\ln u\Big]_4^6$$

$$= \ln 6 - \ln 4 = \ln\frac{3}{2}$$

With a quotient, see if the derivative of the denominator is a constant times the numerator. Use substitution.

Must remember to change the limits.

(e) Choosing $u = (1 + t)$, a basic function is obtained

$$\int_0^3 \frac{1}{\sqrt{1+t}}\,dt = \int_1^4 \frac{1}{\sqrt{u}}\,du$$

$$= \Big[2\sqrt{u}\Big]_1^4$$

$$= 2(\sqrt{4} - \sqrt{1}) = 2$$

Use substitution.

FINDING AREAS AND LENGTHS BY INTEGRATION

KEY POINTS AND DEFINITIONS

- The area under the curve, $y = f(x)$, is given by $\int f(x)dx$.

EXAMPLE 1

- Find the area enclosed by the curve $y = x\sec^2 x$, the x-axis and the lines $x = 0$ and $x = \frac{\pi}{4}$.

SOLUTION

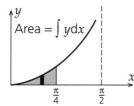

Sketch the graph of the function and show the area to be found. This is a product and use integration by parts with $u = x$ and $\frac{dv}{dx} = \sec^2 x$.

$$\text{Area} = \int_0^{\frac{\pi}{4}} x\sec^2 x\,dx$$

$$\int x\sec^2 x\,dx = x\tan x - \int \tan x\,dx = x\tan x + \ln|\cos x|$$

$$\int_0^{\frac{\pi}{4}} x\sec^2 x\,dx = \left[x\tan x + \ln|\cos x|\right]_0^{\frac{\pi}{4}} = \frac{\pi}{4}\tan\frac{\pi}{4} + \ln\cos\frac{\pi}{4} - \ln\cos 0$$

$$\text{Area} = \frac{\pi}{4} + \ln\frac{1}{\sqrt{2}} = \frac{\pi}{4} - \ln\sqrt{2}$$

Must remember

$\tan\frac{\pi}{4} = 1$, $\cos\frac{\pi}{4} = \frac{1}{\sqrt{2}}$,

$\cos 0 = 1$ and $\ln 1 = 0$.

EXAMPLE 2

- Find the area enclosed by the curve $y = \frac{10}{2x + 5}$, the y-axis and the lines $y = 1$ and $y = 2$.

SOLUTION

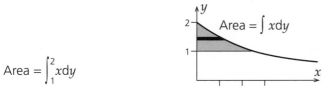

In this case, the area is easily found using a y-integral. To do this, the inverse function is needed.

$$\text{Area} = \int_1^2 x\,dy$$

$$y = \frac{10}{2x + 5} \Rightarrow (2x + 5)y = 10 \Rightarrow 2x = \frac{10}{y} - 5 \Rightarrow x = \frac{5}{y} - \frac{5}{2}$$

$$\text{Area} = \int_1^2\left(\frac{5}{y} - \frac{5}{2}\right)dy = \left[5\ln y - \frac{5}{2}y\right]_1^2 = (5\ln 2 - 5) - \left(5\ln 1 - \frac{5}{2}\right)$$

$$= 5\ln 2 - \frac{5}{2}$$

EXAMPLE 3

- The length of the curve $y = f(x)$ between the points on the curve $(a, f(a))$ and $(b, f(b))$ is given by $s = \int_a^b \sqrt{1 + f'(x)^2}\,dx$. Find the length of the curve $y = x^{\frac{3}{2}}$ between the points on the curve $(1, 1)$ and $(4, 8)$ giving your answer to 4 d.p.

SOLUTION

$$f(x) = x^{\frac{3}{2}} \Rightarrow f'(x) = \frac{3}{2}x^{\frac{1}{2}} \Rightarrow \sqrt{1 + f'(x)^2} = \sqrt{1 + \frac{9}{4}x}$$

$$s = \int_1^4 \sqrt{1 + \frac{9}{4}x}\,dx$$

$$= \int_{\frac{13}{4}}^{10} \sqrt{u} \times \frac{4}{9}\,du = \left[\frac{4}{9} \times \frac{2}{3}u^{\frac{3}{2}}\right]_{\frac{13}{4}}^{10}$$

$$= \frac{8}{27}\left(10\sqrt{10} - \frac{13}{4}\sqrt{\frac{13}{4}}\right) = 7.6337 \text{ (to 4 d.p.)}$$

Use substitution with

$u = 1 + \frac{9}{4}x$ and $\frac{du}{dx} = \frac{9}{4}$.

VOLUMES OF REVOLUTION ABOUT THE x-AXIS

KEY POINTS AND DEFINITIONS

- A volume of revolution is formed when a region is rotated through 360° around an axis, in this case the x-axis.

- The diagram shows a volume formed in this way.

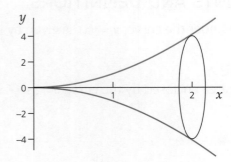

> **MUST REMEMBER ...**
>
> The volume of revolution is given by $\int_a^b \pi y^2 \mathrm{d}x$.

EXAMPLE 1

- The region enclosed by the curve $y = x^2$, the x-axis and the line $x = 5$ is rotated through 360° around the x-axis. Find the volume of the solid that is formed.

SOLUTION

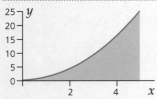

| The diagram shows the region that is to be rotated. | This sketch shows the region that is to be rotated and helps to define the limits of integration. |

| Volume $= \int_0^5 \pi(x^2)^2 \mathrm{d}x$

 $= \int_0^5 \pi x^4 \mathrm{d}x$ | Use the formula $\int_a^b \pi y^2 \mathrm{d}x$ and simplify before integrating. |

| $= \pi\left[\dfrac{x^5}{5}\right]_0^5$

 $= \pi\left(\left(\dfrac{5^5}{5}\right) - 0\right) = 625\pi$ | Integrate and then substitute the limits.
 It is a good idea to leave the answer in terms of π. |

EXAMPLE 2

- Find the volume created when the region enclosed by the curve $y = e^x + 1$, the x- and y-axes and the line $x = 2$ is rotated through 360° around the x-axis.

SOLUTION

| Volume $= \int_0^2 \pi(e^x + 1)^2 \mathrm{d}x$

 $= \pi\int_0^2 (e^{2x} + 2e^x + 1)\mathrm{d}x$ | Use the formula $\int_a^b \pi y^2 \mathrm{d}x$.

 Be careful when expanding the brackets.

 Must remember that $(e^x)^2 = e^{2x}$. |

| $= \pi\left[\dfrac{1}{2}e^{2x} + 2e^x + x\right]_0^2$

 $= \pi\left(\left(\dfrac{1}{2}e^4 + 2e^2 + 2\right) - \left(\dfrac{1}{2} + 2 + 0\right)\right)$

 $= \pi\left(\dfrac{1}{2}e^4 + 2e^2 - \dfrac{1}{2}\right) = 131$ (to 3 s.f.) | Integrate and then simplify the result when the limits of integration have been substituted.

 A numerical value has been calculated. |

VOLUMES OF REVOLUTION ABOUT THE y-AXIS

KEY POINTS AND DEFINITIONS

- In the same way that volumes can be formed by rotating a region around the x-axis, regions can also be formed by revolving regions around the y-axis. The formula below is used to calculate these volumes.

MUST REMEMBER ...

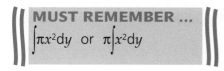

$$\int \pi x^2 \, dy \quad \text{or} \quad \pi \int x^2 \, dy$$

EXAMPLE

- The region enclosed by the lines $y = 2x$, $y = 6$ and the y-axis is rotated through 360° around the y-axis.

   (a) Sketch the region that is rotated around the y-axis.

   (b) Find the volume that is obtained.

SOLUTION

(a) 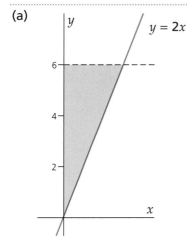	Sketch the region.
(b) $y = 2x$ $x = \dfrac{y}{2}$	Express x in terms of y.
$\text{Volume} = \pi \displaystyle\int_0^6 \left(\frac{y}{2}\right)^2 dy$ $= \pi \displaystyle\int_0^6 \frac{y^2}{4} \, dy$	Form the required integral.
$= \pi \left[\dfrac{y^3}{12}\right]_0^6$	Carry out the integration.
$= \pi \left(\dfrac{6^3}{12}\right) - 0$ $= 18\pi$	Substitute the limits and evaluate to find the actual volume. The answer has been left in terms of π.

LOCATION OF ROOTS BY SIGN CHANGES

KEY POINTS AND DEFINITIONS

- For a continuous function, f, and the interval $[a, b] = a \le x \le b$, if $f(a)$ and $f(b)$ have opposite signs, then $f(x) = 0$ for some value of x in this interval.

MUST REMEMBER ...

Define the point $x = c$ as $c = \dfrac{a+b}{2}$. If $f(a)$ and $f(c)$ have opposite signs, let $c = b$, otherwise let $c = a$. Repeat until the interval $[a, b]$ containing a root of the equation is narrow enough to give the desired accuracy.

This is called the Interval Bisection method.

EXAMPLE 1

- (a) Sketch the graph of $f(x) = 2x^2 + x - 2e^x$.

  (b) Find an interval $[a, b]$ within which the root of $f(x) = 0$ lies where a and b are consecutive integers.

  (c) Use the method of interval bisection to find the roots of $f(x) = 0$ to 2 significant figures.

SOLUTION

(a)

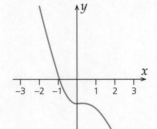

It's a good idea to take a sketch from a graphic calculator.

(b) The root lies in the interval $[-1, 0]$

(c) Choose $a = -1$ and $b = 0$.

n	a	b	c	f(a)	f(b)	f(c)
1	−1	0	−0.5	> 0	< 0	< 0
2	−1	−0.5	−0.75	> 0	< 0	< 0
3	−1	−0.75	−0.875	> 0	< 0	< 0
4	−1	−0.875	−0.9375	> 0	< 0	> 0
5	−0.9375	−0.875	−0.90625	> 0	< 0	< 0
6	−0.9375	−0.90625	−0.921875	> 0	< 0	< 0
7	−0.9375	−0.921875	−0.9296875	> 0	< 0	> 0
8	−0.9296875	−0.921875	−0.92578125	> 0	< 0	< 0
9	−0.9296875	−0.92578125				

The root is −0.93 to 2 significant figures

The interval is now narrow enough to give the answer to the necessary accuracy.

EXAMPLE 2

- Let $[a, a + 1]$ be the starting interval for a method of interval bisection to solve $f(x) = 0$, where a is an integer.

  (a) What will be the maximum error after 1 iteration?
  (b) What will be the maximum error after 5 iterations?
  (c) What will be the maximum error after n iterations?

SOLUTION

(a)

$$a \quad a + \tfrac{1}{2} \quad a + 1$$

As the width of the interval is 1, the actual root must be within $\frac{1}{2}$ of the mid-point. So the error of this approximate solution must be less than or equal to $\frac{1}{2}$.

It is known that there is a sign change in $f(x)$ in the interval $[a, a + 1]$.

(b) After 5 iterations the maximum error is $\left(\dfrac{1}{2}\right)^5 = \dfrac{1}{2^5} = \dfrac{1}{32}$

In each interval, the maximum error is $\frac{1}{2}$ of the previous error.

(c) So after n iterations the maximum error is $\left(\dfrac{1}{2}\right)^n = \dfrac{1}{2^n}$

USING AN ITERATIVE METHOD

KEY POINTS AND DEFINITIONS

- To solve $f(x) = 0$, rearrange into the form $x = g(x)$. The iteration formula $x_{n+1} = g(x_n)$, $n = 0, 1, 2, 3, \ldots$ generates a convergent sequence towards a root α provided $|g'(\alpha)| < 1$ and the initial approximation x_0 is close to α.

EXAMPLE 1

- **(a)** The sequence $x_{n+1} = \sqrt{3x_n + 2}$ with $x_0 = 1$ converges to α. Find α correct to three decimal places.

  (b) Show that α satisfies the equation $x^2 - 3x - 2 = 0$.

SOLUTION

(a) √(3*Ans+2)

2.236067977	3.557913184
2.95096661	3.5600196
3.294373966	3.560907019
3.447190436	3.561280817
3.513057259	3.561438256
3.541069299	3.561504565
3.552915408	

$\alpha = 3.562$ correct to three decimal places

A graphic calculator helps to generate this sequence easily using the ANS key.

(b) $x = \sqrt{3x + 2} \Rightarrow x^2 = 3x + 2$

$\Rightarrow x^2 - 3x - 2 = 0$

At the fixed point of the iterative formula $x = g(x)$.

EXAMPLE 2

- The equation $x + 2\ln x = 0$ has a root in the interval $[0, 1]$. Show that one and only one of the following iterative formulae will converge to that root.

  (a) $x_{n+1} = -2\ln x_n$ **(b)** $x_{n+1} = e^{-\frac{1}{2}x_n}$

  Hence find the root correct to 3 significant figures.

SOLUTION

(a) $g(x) = -2\ln x \Rightarrow g'(x) = -\dfrac{2}{x}$

Within $[0, 1]$ $|g'(x)| \geq 2 \Rightarrow$ divergent scheme

To test the convergence of the formula, consider the size of $g'(x)$ in the interval.

(b) $g(x) = e^{-\frac{1}{2}x} \Rightarrow g'(x) = -\dfrac{1}{2}e^{-\frac{1}{2}x}$

Within $[0, 1]$ $\dfrac{1}{2}e^{-\frac{1}{2}} \leq |g'(x)| \leq \dfrac{1}{2} \Rightarrow$ convergent scheme

e^(−.5*Ans)

1	0.703280563
0.6065306597	0.7035331504
0.73840315	0.7034443042
0.6912860504	0.703475554
0.7077650963	0.7034645624
0.7019574087	0.7034684285
0.7039987458	

The root is 0.703 correct to 3 significant figures

Use this iterative formula to find the root.

CREATING AN ITERATIVE METHOD I

KEY POINTS AND DEFINITIONS

- To find an appropriate iterative method, start with the equation to be solved and rearrange the formula to write $x = g(x)$.

- For convergence, check that $|g'(x)| \leq 1$ in the region close to the root.

EXAMPLE

- **(a)** Show that $f(x) = x^3 + 3x^2 - 7 = 0$ has just one root α between 1 and 2.

  (b) Show that $f(x) = 0$ can be rearranged as $x = \sqrt{\dfrac{a}{x + b}}$, $x \neq -b$ and state the values of a and b.

  The iterative formula $x_{n+1} = \sqrt{\dfrac{a}{x_n + b}}$ is used to find an approximation to α.

  (c) Check that this iterative formula is convergent.

  (d) Taking $x_1 = 2$, find the value of the root correct to two decimal places.

  (e) Write down a value for x_1 for which the iteration formula $x_{n+1} = \sqrt{\dfrac{a}{x_n + b}}$ does NOT produce a valid value for x_2 and justify your answer.

SOLUTION

(a)

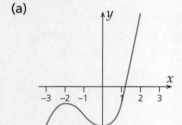

The curve cuts the x-axis once, so there is only one root, which is between 1 and 2.

Draw the graph of $y = f(x)$.

(b) $x^3 + 3x^2 - 7 = 0 \Rightarrow x^2(x + 3) = 7$

$$x^2 = \frac{7}{x + 3}$$

$$x = \sqrt{\frac{7}{x + 3}}$$

$$a = 7 \text{ and } b = 3$$

Rearrange the equation.

(c) $\qquad |g(x)| = \sqrt{\dfrac{7}{x + 3}}$

$$\Rightarrow g'(x) = \frac{-\sqrt{7}}{2(x + 3)^{\frac{3}{2}}}$$

$$\Rightarrow |g'(x)| \leq 0.17 \text{ so this is a convergent scheme}$$

Show that $|g'(x)| \leq 1$ in the interval [1, 2].

(d) $\sqrt{(7/(3+\text{Ans}))}$

1.183215957
1.293581742
1.276847858
1.27934336
1.278970281
1.279026035
Root is 1.28 to two decimal places

Carry out the iteration.

(e) $x_1 = -3$ since division by zero is not possible

Any number < -3 would also be inappropriate, as this would involve the square root of a negative number.

CREATING AN ITERATIVE METHOD II

KEY POINTS AND DEFINITIONS

- Sometimes different rearrangements of the equation are necessary before a convergent scheme is found.

EXAMPLE

- **(a)** Sketch the graph of $y = x^3 - 3x + 1$ and find integer intervals in which each root occurs.

  (b) By choosing suitable forms for the iterative function g(x), use the fixed point iterative method to find these roots of the equation $x^3 - 3x + 1 = 0$ correct to three significant figures.

SOLUTION

(a)

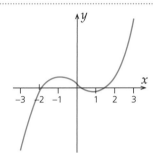

The roots lie in the intervals
[−2, −1], [0, 1] and [1, 2]

(b) $x^3 - 3x + 1 = 0$

$$x = \frac{1}{3}(1 + x^3) \Rightarrow g(x) = \frac{1}{3}(1 + x^3) \Rightarrow g'(x) = x^2$$

For the interval [−2, −1], $1 \le |g'(x)| \le 4 \Rightarrow$ divergent

For the interval [0, 1], $0 \le |g'(x)| \le 1 \Rightarrow$ convergent

For the interval [1, 2], $1 \le |g'(x)| \le 4 \Rightarrow$ divergent

Rearrange the formula to find g(x) and then check the size of $|g'(x)|$ within the interval of the root.

For [0, 1] $x_{n+1} = \frac{1}{3}(1 + x_n^3)$: choose $x_0 = 0$

(1+Ans^3)/3

0.3333333333	0.3472729489
0.3456790123	0.3472935324
0.3471021869	0.3472960148
	So root is 0.347 (to 3 s.f.)

Carry out the iteration for this convergent scheme.

$x = \sqrt[3]{3x - 1} \Rightarrow g(x) = \sqrt[3]{3x - 1} \Rightarrow g'(x) = \dfrac{1}{(3x - 1)^{\frac{2}{3}}}$

For the interval [−2, −1], $0.27 \le |g'(x)| \le 0.40 \Rightarrow$ convergent

For the interval [1, 2], $0.34 \le |g'(x)| \le 0.63 \Rightarrow$ convergent

Find a different rearrangement to produce convergent schemes for the other two intervals.

For [−2, −1], $x_{n+1} = \sqrt[3]{3x_n - 1}$: choose $x_0 = -2$

The sequence is

−1.912931	−1.880141
−1.888835	−1.879599
−1.882057	−1.879446 $\Rightarrow$ root is −1.88

For [1, 2], $x_{n+1} = \sqrt[3]{3x_n - 1}$: choose $x_0 = 1$

The sequence is

1.25992	1.521750
1.406055	1.527672
1.476396	1.530205
1.507985	1.531286 $\Rightarrow$ root is 1.53

There are other rearrangements but the three roots have been found.

COBWEB AND STAIRCASE DIAGRAMS

KEY POINTS AND DEFINITIONS

- A cobweb or staircase diagram is a geometrical representation of the sequence generated by an iterative method.

EXAMPLE 1

- The equation $4x^3 - x - 1 = 0$ has a root in the interval [0, 1]. Use the iteration $x_{n+1} = \sqrt[3]{\dfrac{1 + x_n}{4}}$

  to find the root correct to 3 significant figures. Illustrate your answer using a staircase diagram.

SOLUTION

Choose $x_1 = 0$:

$x_2 = 0.630$

$x_3 = 0.741$

$x_4 = 0.758$

$x_5 = 0.760$

$x_6 = 0.761$

$x_7 = 0.761 \Rightarrow$ root is 0.761 to 3 significant figures

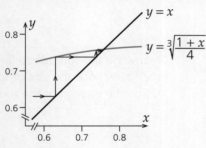

Carry out the iteration.

Each step gets closer to the root.

EXAMPLE 2

- The equation $8 - 3x - 2x^3 = 0$ has a root in the interval [1, 2]. Use the iteration $x_{n+1} = \sqrt[3]{4 - 1.5x_n}$ to find the root correct to 3 significant figures. Illustrate your answer using a cobweb diagram.

SOLUTION

Choose $x_1 = 1$:

$x_2 = 1.357$

$x_3 = 1.252$

$x_4 = 1.285$

$x_5 = 1.275$

$x_6 = 1.278$

$x_7 = 1.277 \Rightarrow$ root is 1.28 to 3 significant figures

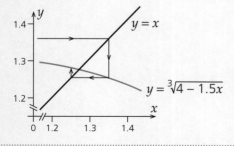

The iterations spiral around the root, getting closer to it.

THE NEWTON RAPHSON METHOD

KEY POINTS AND DEFINITIONS

- To solve $f(x) = 0$, find $f'(x)$ and use the iteration:

$$x_{n+1} = x_n - \frac{f(x_n)}{f'(x_n)}, \quad n = 0, 1, 2, \ldots$$

which generates a convergent sequence towards a root α, provided the initial approximation x_0 is close to α.

EXAMPLE 1

- Use the Newton Raphson method with initial approximation 1.5 to find, correct to 2 decimal places, the root of the equation $x^3 - x^2 - 2 = 0$ which lies between 1 and 2.

SOLUTION

$f(x) = x^3 - x^2 - 2$

$f'(x) = 3x^2 - 2x$ Differentiate to find $f'(x)$.

$x_{n+1} = x_n - \dfrac{x_n^3 - x_n^2 - 2}{3x_n^2 - 2x_n}$ Apply the formula.

$x_1 = 1.5$:

$x_2 = 1.73333; \ x_3 = 1.6967; \ x_4 = 1.6956; \ x_5 = 1.6956$

$\Rightarrow$ root is 1.70 to 2 decimal places

EXAMPLE 2

- **(a)** Sketch the graph of $y = x - 1 + \dfrac{4}{x^2}$.

(b) Use the Newton Raphson iteration to find the only root of the equation $x + \dfrac{4}{x^2} = 1$, with $x_0 = -1$ correct to 2 decimal places.

(c) What problems are encountered by taking:
  (i) $x_0 = 2$;
  (ii) $x_0 > 0, \ x_0 \neq 2$?

SOLUTION

(a)

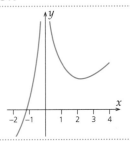

Root is in interval $[-2, -1]$.

(b) $f(x) = x - 1 + \dfrac{4}{x^2} \Rightarrow f'(x) = 1 - \dfrac{8}{x^3}$ Differentiate to find $f'(x)$.

$x_{n+1} = x_n - \dfrac{x_n - 1 + \dfrac{4}{x_n^2}}{1 - \dfrac{8}{x_n^3}}$ Apply the formula.

$x_0 = -1 \Rightarrow x_1 = -1.2222; \ x_2 = -1.3068; \ x_3 = -1.3145; \ x_4 = -1.3146$

$\Rightarrow$ root is -1.31 to 2 decimal places

(c) $x_0 = 2 \Rightarrow f'(2) = 1 - \dfrac{8}{2^3} = 0$ so iterative scheme is divergent

For $x_0 > 0, \ x_0 \neq 2$ the first few iterations suggest that the scheme will diverge but then the scheme converges.

OCR(MEI) C3

THE MID-ORDINATE RULE FOR INTEGRATION

KEY POINTS AND DEFINITIONS

- The mid-ordinate rule for integration approximates a region under a graph by a number of rectangles each of equal width. The sum of the areas of the rectangles is an approximation to the required area.

- The height of a rectangle is the value of the function at the mid-point of the rectangle.

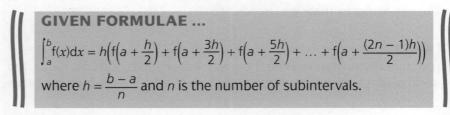

GIVEN FORMULAE ...

$$\int_a^b f(x)dx = h\left(f\left(a + \frac{h}{2}\right) + f\left(a + \frac{3h}{2}\right) + f\left(a + \frac{5h}{2}\right) + \ldots + f\left(a + \frac{(2n-1)h}{2}\right)\right)$$

where $h = \dfrac{b-a}{n}$ and n is the number of subintervals.

EXAMPLE 1

- **(a)** Use the mid-point rule to find $\int_0^1 e^{x^2}dx$ using a step size of 0.2.

  (b) Use sketch graphs to show the exact value and approximate values of the integral.

SOLUTION

(a)

x	0.1	0.3	0.5	0.7	0.9
y	1.01005	1.09417	1.28403	1.63232	2.24791

Create a table of values. Must remember to use the mid-ordinates!

$$\int_0^1 e^{x^2}dx \approx 0.2 \times (1.01005 + 1.09417 + 1.28403 + 1.63232 + 2.24791)$$

$$= 1.4537$$

Substitute the values from the table into the formula.

(b)

EXAMPLE 2

- Calculate the error when the mid-ordinate rule is applied to the integral $\int_a^b (mx + c)dx$ where m and c are constants.

SOLUTION

x	$\dfrac{a+b}{2}$
y	$m\dfrac{(a+b)}{2} + c$

Find the y-coordinate.

Using the mid-ordinate rule:
$$\int_a^b (mx + c)dx = (b-a)\left(\frac{m(a+b)}{2} + c\right) = \frac{m(b^2 - a^2)}{2} + c(b-a)$$

Apply the formula, using one rectangle of width $(b-a)$.

Exact value:
$$\int_a^b (mx + c)dx = \left[m\frac{x^2}{2} + cx\right]_a^b = m\left(\frac{b^2}{2} - \frac{a^2}{2}\right) + c(b-a)$$

There is no error in the mid-ordinate rule for a linear function.

Integrate directly and substitute the limits.

SIMPSON'S RULE FOR INTEGRATION

KEY POINTS AND DEFINITIONS

- Simpson's rule can be used to estimate the value of an integral $\int_a^b f(x)dx$.

- It is based on approximating the function $f(x)$ by a series of parabolas or quadratic approximations.

- The number of intervals for the subdivision of the interval $[a, b]$ must be even.

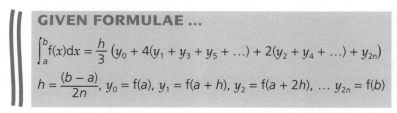

GIVEN FORMULAE ...

$$\int_a^b f(x)dx = \frac{h}{3}\left(y_0 + 4(y_1 + y_3 + y_5 + \ldots) + 2(y_2 + y_4 + \ldots) + y_{2n}\right)$$

$$h = \frac{(b-a)}{2n}, \ y_0 = f(a), \ y_1 = f(a+h), \ y_2 = f(a+2h), \ \ldots \ y_{2n} = f(b)$$

EXAMPLE 1

- **(a)** Use Simpson's rule to find $\int_0^4 \frac{1}{1+x^2}dx$ using 8 subintervals.

  (b) Use the substitution $x = \tan u$ to find an exact value of the integral in part **(a)**.

  (c) Hence find the percentage error in using Simpson's rule to approximate the integral.

SOLUTION

(a) With 8 subintervals, $a = 0$ and $b = 4$, $h = 0.5$	Create a table of values.

x	0	0.5	1	1.5	2	2.5	3	3.5	4
y	1	0.8	0.5	0.307692	0.2	0.137931	0.1	0.075472	0.058824

$\int_0^4 \frac{1}{1+x^2}dx \approx \frac{0.5}{3}(1 + 4(0.8 + 0.307692 + 0.137931 + 0.075472) +$ $2(0.5 + 0.2 + 0.1) + 0.058824)$ $= 1.32387$	Substitute the values from the table into the formula.
(b) With $x = \tan u$, $\frac{dx}{du} = \sec^2 u$ and $1 + x^2 = 1 + \tan^2 u = \sec^2 u$	Use indirect substitution.
$\int_0^4 \frac{1}{1+x^2}dx = \int_0^{\tan^{-1}4} du = \tan^{-1} 4 = 1.32582$	
(c) Percentage error in approx solution $= \left(\frac{1.32582 - 1.32387}{1.32582}\right) \times 100$ $= 0.15\%$	Percentage error $= \frac{\text{Error}}{\text{Exact value}} \times 100\%$.

EXAMPLE 2

- During the launch of a rocket, the speed was noted every second for 10 seconds and the following table of values obtained:

Time(s)	0	1	2	3	4	5	6	7	8	9	10
Speed(kmh^{-1})	0	32	80	128	176	224	272	320	368	400	448

Use Simpson's rule to estimate the distance travelled by the rocket during the first 10 seconds.

SOLUTION

There are 10 intervals of width 1 second $= \frac{1}{3600}$ hour	Always check that the number of intervals is even. Must remember that distance = speed × time.
Distance $= \frac{\frac{1}{3600}}{3}(0 + 4(32 + 128 + 224 + 320 + 400) + 2(80 + 176$ $+ 272 + 368) + 448)$ $= 0.616$ km	

THE FACTOR THEOREM FOR DIVISORS OF THE FORM $(ax - b)$

KEY POINTS AND DEFINITIONS

- The factor theorem states that $(ax - b)$ is a factor of the polynomial $f(x)$ if, and only if, $f\left(\dfrac{b}{a}\right) = 0$.
- This result can be used to help factor polynomials.

EXAMPLE 1

- Show that $(2x - 5)$ is a factor of $f(x) = 4x^3 - 12x^2 - x + 15$.

SOLUTION

$f\left(\dfrac{5}{2}\right) = 4\left(\dfrac{5}{2}\right)^3 - 12\left(\dfrac{5}{2}\right)^2 - \dfrac{5}{2} + 15$	Substitute $x = \dfrac{5}{2}$, to see if $(2x - 5)$ is a factor of $f(x)$.
$\qquad = \dfrac{125}{2} - 75 - \dfrac{5}{2} + 15$	
$\qquad = 0$	
So $(2x - 5)$ is a factor of $f(x)$.	State the conclusion.

EXAMPLE 2

- The polynomial, $p(x) = 6x^3 - 7x^2 + ax + b$ has factors $(2x - 7)$ and $(3x + 1)$. Find a and b.

SOLUTION

$p\left(\dfrac{7}{2}\right) = 0$	Apply the factor theorem to the first factor to form an equation that contains a and b.
$6\left(\dfrac{7}{2}\right)^3 - 7\left(\dfrac{7}{2}\right)^2 + a\left(\dfrac{7}{2}\right) + b = 0$	
$\dfrac{1029}{4} - \dfrac{343}{4} + \dfrac{7a}{2} + b = 0$	
$343 + 7a + 2b = 0$	
$p\left(-\dfrac{1}{3}\right) = 0$	Repeat with the second factor. As this is $(3x + 1)$, consider $p\left(-\dfrac{1}{3}\right)$.
$6\left(-\dfrac{1}{3}\right)^3 - 7\left(-\dfrac{1}{3}\right)^2 + a\left(-\dfrac{1}{3}\right) + b = 0$	
$-\dfrac{2}{9} - \dfrac{7}{9} - \dfrac{a}{3} + b = 0$	
$-3 - a + 3b = 0$	
$343 + 7a + 2b = 0$	Solve the simultaneous equations obtained above. b has been found first.
$-21 - 7a + 21b = 0$	
$322 + 23b = 0$	
$b = \dfrac{-322}{23} = -14$	
$-3 - a + 3 \times (-14) = 0$	Substitute the value of b into one equation and find a.
$a = -45$	

THE REMAINDER THEOREM FOR DIVISORS OF THE FORM $(ax - b)$

KEY POINTS AND DEFINITIONS

- The remainder theorem states that when a polynomial f(x) is divided by $(ax - b)$, the remainder is equal to $f\left(\dfrac{b}{a}\right)$.

EXAMPLE 1
- Find the remainder when p(x) = $3x^2 + 8x - 7$ is divided by $(3x - 2)$.

SOLUTION

$p\left(\dfrac{2}{3}\right) = 3\left(\dfrac{2}{3}\right)^2 + 8\left(\dfrac{2}{3}\right) - 7$ $= \dfrac{4}{3} + \dfrac{16}{3} - 7$ $= -\dfrac{1}{3}$	Evaluate $p\left(\dfrac{2}{3}\right)$ to find the remainder.

EXAMPLE 2
- The polynomial q(x) = $4x^3 + ax^2 + bx - 12$ is such that it has remainder 78 when divided by $(2x - 5)$ and $(x + 4)$ is a factor. Find a and b.

SOLUTION

$q(-4) = 0$ $4 \times (-4)^3 + a \times (-4)^2 + b \times (-4) - 12 = 0$ $-256 + 16a - 4b - 12 = 0$ $67 - 4a + b = 0$	Use the factor theorem with $(x + 4)$ to form one equation involving a and b.
$q\left(\dfrac{5}{2}\right) = 78$ $4 \times \left(\dfrac{5}{2}\right)^3 + a \times \left(\dfrac{5}{2}\right)^2 + b \times \left(\dfrac{5}{2}\right) - 12 = 78$ $\dfrac{125}{2} + \dfrac{25a}{4} + \dfrac{5b}{2} - 12 = 78$ $-110 + 25a + 10b = 0$	Use the remainder theorem with $(2x - 5)$ to form a second equation involving a and b.
$670 - 40a + 10b = 0$ $\underline{-110 + 25a + 10b = 0}$ (Subtracting) $780 - 65a = 0$ $a = \dfrac{780}{65} = 12$	Solve the simultaneous equations to find a.
$67 - 4 \times 12 + b = 0$ $b = -19$	Substitute the value of a and then find b.

ADDITION AND SUBTRACTION OF RATIONAL FUNCTIONS

KEY POINTS AND DEFINITIONS

- When adding or subtracting rational functions, make sure that they have a common denominator. The fractions can then be added or subtracted and any possible simplification carried out.

EXAMPLE 1

- Express $\dfrac{1}{x+9} + \dfrac{1}{x+6}$ as a single fraction.

SOLUTION

$$\frac{1}{x+9} + \frac{1}{x+6} = \frac{x+6}{(x+9)(x+6)} + \frac{x+9}{(x+9)(x+6)}$$

Use a common denominator of $(x+9)(x+6)$.

$$= \frac{2x+15}{(x+9)(x+6)}$$

Add the numerators.

EXAMPLE 2

- Express $\dfrac{x}{x^2-25} - \dfrac{1}{x^2+5x}$ as a single fraction.

SOLUTION

$$\frac{x}{x^2-25} - \frac{1}{x^2+5x} = \frac{x}{(x-5)(x+5)} - \frac{1}{x(x+5)}$$

First factorise the denominators and then identify $x(x-5)(x+5)$ as the common denominator.

$$= \frac{x^2}{x(x-5)(x+5)} - \frac{x-5}{x(x-5)(x+5)}$$

$$= \frac{x^2-x+5}{x(x-5)(x+5)}$$

Subtract the numerators..

EXAMPLE 3

- Express $\dfrac{x}{x+2} - \dfrac{5x+14}{x^2+2x}$ in the form $a - \dfrac{b}{x}$, where a and b are constants.

SOLUTION

$$\frac{x}{x+2} - \frac{5x+14}{x^2+2x} = \frac{x}{x+2} - \frac{5x+14}{x(x+2)}$$

Factorise the denominators.

The denominator of the second fraction, $x(x+2)$, can be used as the common denominator.

$$= \frac{x^2}{x(x+2)} - \frac{5x+14}{x(x+2)}$$

$$= \frac{x^2-5x-14}{x(x+2)}$$

Subtract the numerators.

$$= \frac{(x+2)(x-7)}{x(x+2)}$$

Factorise the numerators.

$$= \frac{x-7}{x}$$

$$= \frac{x}{x} - \frac{7}{x}$$

$$= 1 - \frac{7}{x}$$

Cancel the common factor $(x+2)$. Then split into two fractions to obtain the required result with $a = 1$ and $b = 7$.

MULTIPLYING AND DIVIDING RATIONAL FUNCTIONS

KEY POINTS AND DEFINITIONS

- When multiplying and dividing rational functions, apply the basic rules of fractions. In addition, factorise expressions and cancel common factors.

MUST REMEMBER …

Basic rules of fractions:

$$\frac{a}{b} \times \frac{c}{d} = \frac{a \times c}{b \times d} \text{ and } \frac{a}{b} \div \frac{c}{d} = \frac{a}{b} \times \frac{d}{c} = \frac{a \times d}{b \times c}$$

EXAMPLE 1

- Simplify $\dfrac{5x^2 - 80}{2x^2 + 2x - 24}$.

SOLUTION

$\dfrac{5x^2 - 80}{2x^2 + 2x - 24} = \dfrac{5(x^2 - 16)}{2(x^2 + x - 12)}$	Factorise the numerator and the denominator.
$= \dfrac{5(x + 4)(x - 4)}{2(x + 4)(x - 3)}$	
$= \dfrac{5(x - 4)}{2(x - 3)}$	Cancel out the common factor $(x + 4)$.

EXAMPLE 2

- Simplify $\dfrac{x^2 + 6x}{x^2 - 1} \times \dfrac{x + 1}{x^2 + 9x + 18}$.

SOLUTION

$\dfrac{x^2 + 6x}{x^2 - 1} \times \dfrac{x + 1}{x^2 + 9x + 18} = \dfrac{x(x + 6)}{(x + 1)(x - 1)} \times \dfrac{(x + 1)}{(x + 6)(x + 3)}$	Factorise and multiply to bring the factors together into one fraction.
$= \dfrac{x(x + 6)(x + 1)}{(x + 1)(x - 1)(x + 6)(x + 3)}$	
$= \dfrac{x}{(x - 1)(x + 3)}$	The common factors $(x + 6)$ and $(x + 1)$ can be cancelled.

EXAMPLE 3

- Simplify $\dfrac{x^2 - 4}{x^2 + 3x} \div \dfrac{x^2 + 2x}{x^2 - 9}$.

SOLUTION

$\dfrac{x^2 - 4}{x^2 + 3x} \div \dfrac{x^2 + 2x}{x^2 - 9} = \dfrac{x^2 - 4}{x^2 + 3x} \times \dfrac{x^2 - 9}{x^2 + 2x}$	First invert the second fraction and multiply.
$= \dfrac{(x - 2)(x + 2)}{x(x + 3)} \times \dfrac{(x - 3)(x + 3)}{x(x + 2)}$	Factor the terms and bring together into a single fraction.
$= \dfrac{(x - 2)(x + 2)(x - 3)(x + 3)}{x^2(x + 3)(x + 2)}$	
$= \dfrac{(x - 2)(x - 3)}{x^2}$	Cancel the common factors.

RATIONAL FUNCTIONS AND GRAPHS I

AQA
C3

Edexcel
C3/4

OCR
C3

OCR(MEI)
C4

WJEC
C3

KEY POINTS AND DEFINITIONS

- When sketching the graph of a rational function, look for:
  - Vertical asymptotes, where the denominator is zero;
  - Horizontal asymptotes, by considering the function for large positive or negative x;
  - Intersections with the axes, when $x = 0$ and when $y = 0$;
  - Turning or stationary points, when $\frac{dy}{dx} = 0$.

EXAMPLE

- Sketch the graph of $y = \dfrac{1}{x+2}$.

SOLUTION

Vertical asymptote: $$x + 2 = 0$$ $$x = -2$$	Consider any vertical asymptotes.
Horizontal asymptote: As $x \rightarrow +\infty$, $y \rightarrow 0$ from above. As $x \rightarrow -\infty$, $y \rightarrow 0$ from below. So $y = 0$ is a horizontal asymptote.	Consider any horizontal asymptotes.
When $x = 0$, $y = \frac{1}{2}$ so $\left(0, \frac{1}{2}\right)$ is an intersection with the y-axis.	Let $x = 0$.
When $y = 0$, $\frac{1}{x+2} = 0$. As this equation has no solution, there will be no intersection with the x-axis.	Let $y = 0$.
$\frac{dy}{dx} = \frac{-1}{(x+2)^2}$ As this cannot be zero there are no turning points.	Consider any turning points.
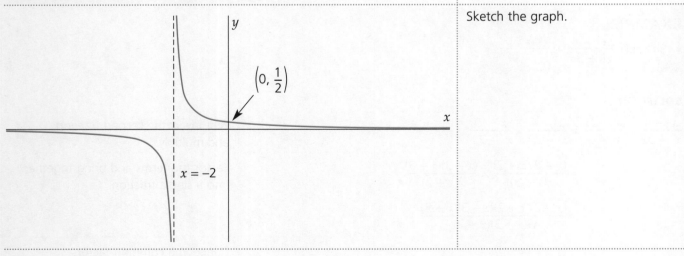	Sketch the graph.

RATIONAL FUNCTIONS AND GRAPHS II

KEY POINTS AND DEFINITIONS

- When sketching graphs, remember to look for asymptotes, intersections with the axes and stationary points.

EXAMPLE

- Sketch the graph of $y = \dfrac{1}{x^2 - 2x - 3}$.

SOLUTION

Vertical asymptote: $y = \dfrac{1}{x^2 - 2x - 3} = \dfrac{1}{(x + 1)(x - 3)}$ Asymptotes are $x = -1$ and $x = 3$.	Consider any vertical asymptotes.
Horizontal asymptote: As $x \to +\infty$, $y \to 0$ from above. As $x \to -\infty$, $y \to 0$ from above. So $y = 0$ is a horizontal asymptote.	Consider any horizontal asymptotes.
When $x = 0$, $y = -\dfrac{1}{3}$ so $\left(0, -\dfrac{1}{3}\right)$ is an intersection with the y-axis.	Let $x = 0$.
When $y = 0$, $\dfrac{1}{x^2 - 2x - 3} = 0$ This is impossible, so there are no intersections with the x-axis.	Let $y = 0$.
$\dfrac{dy}{dx} = \dfrac{-(2x - 2)}{(x + 1)^2 (x - 3)^2}$ There is a turning point when $x = 1$. The coordinates of this point are $\left(1, -\dfrac{1}{4}\right)$.	Consider any turning points.
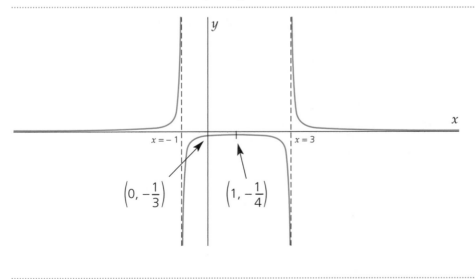	Sketch the graph.

ALGEBRAIC LONG DIVISION

KEY POINTS AND DEFINITIONS

- Algebraic long division is a useful technique when working with polynomials. Following a long division:

  Polynomial = Divisor × Quotient + Remainder

MUST REMEMBER ...

Polynomial = Divisor × Quotient + Remainder

or $\dfrac{\text{Polynomial}}{\text{Divisor}} = \text{Quotient} + \dfrac{\text{Remainder}}{\text{Divisor}}$

EXAMPLE 1

- Divide $4x^3 + 6x^2 - 12x + 8$ by $2x - 1$.

SOLUTION

$$
\begin{array}{r}
2x^2 + 4x - 4 \\
2x - 1 \overline{) 4x^3 + 6x^2 - 12x + 8} \\
\underline{4x^3 - 2x^2} \\
8x^2 - 12x \\
\underline{8x^2 - 4x} \\
-8x + 8 \\
\underline{-8x + 4} \\
4
\end{array}
$$

Carry out the long division, multiplying $(2x - 1)$ by: $2x^2$, $4x$ and then -4.

The divisor is $(2x - 1)$, the quotient is $2x^2 + 4x - 4$ and the remainder is 4.

$4x^3 + 6x^2 - 12x + 8 = (2x - 1)(2x^2 + 4x - 4) + 4$

or

$\dfrac{4x^3 + 6x^2 - 12x + 8}{(2x - 1)} = (2x^2 + 4x - 4) + \dfrac{4}{(2x - 1)}$

Write the result in one of these two formats.

EXAMPLE 2

- Show that $\dfrac{x^3 - 4}{x - 1} = Ax^2 + Bx + C + \dfrac{D}{x - 1}$, finding the values of A, B, C and D.

SOLUTION

$$
\begin{array}{r}
x^2 + x + 1 \\
x - 1 \overline{) x^3 - 4} \\
\underline{x^3 - x^2} \\
x^2 \\
\underline{x^2 - x} \\
x - 4 \\
\underline{x - 1} \\
-3
\end{array}
$$

When carrying out the long division, remember that $x^3 - 4 = x^3 + 0x^2 + 0x - 4$.

$\dfrac{x^3 - 4}{x - 1} = x^2 + x + 1 + \dfrac{-3}{x - 1}$

Write the result in the standard form.

$A = B = C = 1$ and $D = -3$

State the values of A, B, C and D.

PARTIAL FRACTIONS I

KEY POINTS AND DEFINITIONS

- When the largest power in the numerator of a rational function is less than the largest power in the denominator, the fraction can be written in the partial fraction format.

MUST REMEMBER ...

$$\frac{ax + b}{(c + dx)(e + fx)} = \frac{A}{c + dx} + \frac{B}{e + fx}$$

and $\dfrac{ax^2 + bx + c}{(d + ex)(f + gx)^2}$

$$= \frac{A}{d + ex} + \frac{B}{f + gx} + \frac{C}{(f + gx)^2}$$

EXAMPLE 1

- Express $\dfrac{4}{(x - 2)(x + 1)}$ in partial fraction form.

SOLUTION

$\dfrac{4}{(x - 2)(x + 1)} = \dfrac{A}{x - 2} + \dfrac{B}{x + 1}$	Select the correct form for the partial fractions.
$= \dfrac{A(x + 1) + B(x - 2)}{(x - 2)(x + 1)}$	Create a single fraction with the same denominator as the original expression.
$4 = A(x + 1) + B(x - 2)$	Compare the numerators.
If $x = -1$, then $4 = -3B$, so $B = -\dfrac{4}{3}$.	Substitute $x = -1$ to obtain the value of B.
If $x = 2$, then $4 = 3A$, so $A = \dfrac{4}{3}$.	Substitute $x = 2$ to obtain the value of A.
Then $\dfrac{4}{(x - 2)(x + 1)} = \dfrac{4}{3(x - 2)} - \dfrac{4}{3(x + 1)}$	State the final result.

EXAMPLE 2

- Express $\dfrac{x + 1}{(x - 4)(x - 1)^2}$ in partial fraction form.

SOLUTION

$\dfrac{x + 1}{(x - 4)(x - 1)^2} = \dfrac{A}{x - 4} + \dfrac{B}{x - 1} + \dfrac{C}{(x - 1)^2}$	Use the correct format with three fractions.
$= \dfrac{A(x - 1)^2 + B(x - 1)(x - 4) + C(x - 4)}{(x - 4)(x - 1)^2}$	Make the denominator the same for both sides.
$x + 1 = A(x - 1)^2 + B(x - 1)(x - 4) + C(x - 4)$	Compare the numerators.
If $x = 1$, then $2 = -3C$ so $C = -\dfrac{2}{3}$.	Substitute $x = 1$ to find the value of C.
If $x = 4$, then $5 = 9A$ so $A = \dfrac{5}{9}$.	Substitute $x = 4$ to find the value of A.
Comparing the coefficients of x^2 gives: $0 = A + B$ so that $B = -A = -\dfrac{5}{9}$.	An alternative approach is to substitute $x = 0$ and solve the equation for B.
$\dfrac{x + 1}{(x - 4)(x - 1)^2} = \dfrac{5}{9(x - 4)} - \dfrac{5}{9(x - 1)} - \dfrac{2}{3(x - 1)^2}$	State the final result.

PARTIAL FRACTIONS II

KEY POINTS AND DEFINITIONS

- When the highest power of the numerator is equal to the highest power in the denominator, the fraction can be written as a constant plus partial fractions.

  For example: $\dfrac{2x^2 + 6x - 28}{(x - 3)(x + 5)} = 2 + \dfrac{1}{x - 3} + \dfrac{1}{x + 5}$

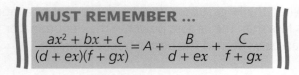

MUST REMEMBER ...

$$\frac{ax^2 + bx + c}{(d + ex)(f + gx)} = A + \frac{B}{d + ex} + \frac{C}{f + gx}$$

EXAMPLE 1

- Write $\dfrac{2x + 1}{x - 2}$ in the form $A + \dfrac{B}{x - 2}$.

SOLUTION

$\dfrac{2x + 1}{x - 2} = A + \dfrac{B}{x - 2}$. $\qquad = \dfrac{(x - 2)A + B}{x - 2}$	Create a single fraction with $(x - 2)$ as the denominator.
$2x + 1 = (x - 2)A + B$	Compare the numerators.
If $x = 2$, then $B = 5$.	Substitute $x = 2$ to find the value of B.
Comparing the coefficients of x gives $A = 2$.	Compare the coefficients or substitute $x = 0$ to obtain the value of A.
$\dfrac{2x + 1}{x - 2} = 2 + \dfrac{5}{x - 2}$	State the final result.

EXAMPLE 2

- Write $\dfrac{x^2}{(x - 5)(x + 2)}$ in the form $A + \dfrac{B}{x - 5} + \dfrac{C}{x + 2}$.

SOLUTION

$\dfrac{x^2}{(x - 5)(x + 2)} = A + \dfrac{B}{x - 5} + \dfrac{C}{x + 2}$ $\qquad = \dfrac{A(x - 5)(x + 2) + B(x + 2) + C(x - 5)}{(x - 5)(x + 2)}$	Write the expression as a single fraction with denominator $(x - 5)(x + 2)$.
$x^2 = A(x - 5)(x + 2) + B(x + 2) + C(x - 5)$	Compare the numerators.
If $x = 5$, then $25 = 7B$, so $B = \dfrac{25}{7}$	Substitute $x = 5$ to find B.
If $x = -2$, then $4 = -7C$, so $C = -\dfrac{4}{7}$.	Substitute $x = -2$ to find C.
Compare the coefficients of x^2 to give $A = 1$.	Compare the coefficients of x^2 to find A. Alternatively substitute $x = 0$.
$\dfrac{x^2}{(x - 5)(x + 2)} = 1 + \dfrac{25}{7(x - 5)} - \dfrac{4}{7(x + 2)}$	State the final result.

PARTIAL FRACTIONS III

KEY POINTS AND DEFINITIONS

- When one of the factors is a quadratic that does not factorise, then a term of the form $\dfrac{Ax + B}{(ax^2 + b)}$ must be included.

EXAMPLE

- Write $\dfrac{1}{(x + 1)(x^2 + 2)}$ as the sum of two partial fractions.

SOLUTION

$\dfrac{1}{(x + 1)(x^2 + 2)} = \dfrac{A}{x + 1} + \dfrac{Bx + C}{x^2 + 2}$	Write in the correct partial fraction format.
$= \dfrac{A(x^2 + 2) + (Bx + C)(x + 1)}{(x + 1)(x^2 + 2)}$	Write the fraction as one with the same denominator as the original expression.
$A(x^2 + 2) + (Bx + C)(x + 1) = 1$	Compare the numerators.
If $x = -1$, $3A = 1$, so $A = \dfrac{1}{3}$	Substitute $x = -1$ to find the value of A.
Either $(A + B)x^2 + (B + C)x + (2A + C) = 1$ $2A + C = 1$ $\dfrac{2}{3} + C = 1$ $C = \dfrac{1}{3}$ and $\qquad B + C = 0$ $B + \dfrac{1}{3} = 0$ $B = -\dfrac{1}{3}$	Either multiply out the numerator and compare coefficients to find B and C.
Or $\qquad$ If $x = 0$, $2A + C = 1$ $\dfrac{2}{3} + C = 1$ $C = \dfrac{1}{3}$ If $x = 1$, $3A + 2B + 2C = 1$ $1 + 2B + \dfrac{2}{3} = 1$ $B = -\dfrac{1}{3}$	Or substitute two values for x and solve the resulting equations to find B and C.
$\dfrac{1}{(x + 1)(x^2 + 2)} = \dfrac{1}{3(x + 1)} + \dfrac{-x + 1}{3(x^2 + 2)}$ $= \dfrac{1}{3(x + 1)} + \dfrac{1 - x}{3(x^2 + 2)}$	State the final result.

OCR(MEI) C4

PARAMETRIC EQUATIONS OF CURVES

KEY POINTS AND DEFINITIONS

- If a curve is defined parametrically, then both x and y can be written as functions of a parameter, which is often written as t.

EXAMPLE 1

- A curve is defined parametrically as $x = t + 7$ and $y = (t + 1)^2$.

  (a) Show that the point with coordinates $(8, 4)$ lies on the curve.

  (b) Find the two possible values of x for which $y = 64$.

SOLUTION

(a) If $x = 8$, then $$8 = t + 7$$ $$t = 8 - 7 = 1$$	Substitute $x = 8$ to form an equation that can be solved to find t.
$$y = (1 + 1)^2$$ $$= 2^2$$ $$= 4$$	Substitute this value of t to find y.
So the point with coordinates $(8, 4)$ does lie on the curve.	State the conclusion.
(b) $(t + 1)^2 = 64$	Use $y = 64$ to form an equation.
$$t + 1 = \pm 8$$ $$t = -1 \pm 8$$ $$t = 7 \text{ or } t = -9$$	Solve this equation to find two values for t.
$$x = 7 + 7 = 14$$ or $\quad x = -9 + 7 = -2$	Calculate the corresponding values of x.

EXAMPLE 2

- A curve is defined parametrically as $x = t^2 - 1$ and $y = 2t + 10$. Find the coordinates of the points where the curve intersects the line with equation $y = 2x$.

SOLUTION

$$y = 2x$$ $$2t + 10 = 2(t^2 - 1)$$ $$2t^2 - 2t - 12 = 0$$	Use the relationship $y = 2x$ to form a quadratic equation in t.
$$t^2 - t - 6 = 0$$ $$(t - 3)(t + 2) = 0$$ $$t = 3 \text{ or } t = -2$$	Solve this quadratic equation.
$t = 3$ gives $x = 3^2 - 1 = 8$ and $y = 2 \times 3 + 10 = 16$ So one point of intersection is $(8, 16)$.	Use $t = 3$ to find the coordinates of one point.
$t = -2$ gives $x = (-2)^2 - 1 = 3$ and $y = 2 \times (-2) + 10 = 6$ So the other point of intersection is $(3, 6)$.	Use $t = -2$ to find the coordinates of the other point.

CONVERSION FROM PARAMETRIC TO CARTESIAN FORM

KEY POINTS AND DEFINITIONS

- The Cartesian equation of a curve directly links x and y. To obtain this, eliminate t from the parametric equations. Often this can be done by expressing t in terms of x and then substituting for t in the expression for y.

EXAMPLE 1

- A curve has parametric equation $x = 3t - 1$ and $y = \frac{1}{t^2}$. Find the Cartesian equation of this curve.

SOLUTION

$x = 3t - 1$ $3t = x + 1$ $t = \frac{x + 1}{3}$	Make t the subject of the expression for x.
$y = \dfrac{1}{\left(\dfrac{x + 1}{3}\right)^2} = \left(\dfrac{3}{x + 1}\right)^2 = \dfrac{9}{(x + 1)^2}$	Use this to substitute for t in the expression for y. Then simplify as much as possible.

EXAMPLE 2

- If $x = \frac{1}{t + 2}$ and $y = \frac{t - 1}{t + 1}$, express y in terms of x.

SOLUTION

$x = \dfrac{1}{t + 2}$ $t + 2 = \dfrac{1}{x}$ $t = \dfrac{1}{x} - 2$	Make t the subject of the expression for x.
$y = \dfrac{\dfrac{1}{x} - 2 - 1}{\dfrac{1}{x} - 2 + 1} = \dfrac{\dfrac{1}{x} - 3}{\dfrac{1}{x} - 1} = \dfrac{1 - 3x}{1 - x}$	Use this to substitute for t in the expression for y. Then simplify as much as possible.

EXAMPLE 3

- A curve has parametric equation $x = 3\sin t$ and $y = 3\cos t$. Find the Cartesian equation of this curve.

SOLUTION

$x^2 + y^2 = 9\sin^2 t + 9\cos^2 t$ $\quad\quad = 9(\sin^2 t + \cos^2 t)$ $x^2 + y^2 = 9$	Here use the fact that $\sin^2 t + \cos^2 t = 1$ to eliminate t.

BINOMIAL SERIES $(1 + x)^n$ FOR ANY EXPONENT I

AQA C4

Edexcel C4

OCR C4

OCR(MEI) C4

WJEC C4

KEY POINTS AND DEFINITIONS

- Must be able to expand expressions of the form $(1 + x)^n$ for any value of n.

- This series is only valid if $|x| < 1$ which can also be written as $-1 < x < 1$.

- Examples below involve the case when n is a negative integer.

GIVEN FORMULAE ...

$$(1 + x)^n = 1 + nx + \frac{n(n-1)x^2}{2!} + \frac{n(n-1)(n-2)x^3}{3!} + \dots$$

EXAMPLE 1

- (a) Find the first 4 terms of the binomial expansion of $(1 + x)^{-3}$.

  (b) State the range of values of x for which the expansion is valid.

SOLUTION

(a) $(1 + x)^{-3} = 1 + (-3)x + \frac{(-3)(-4)x^2}{2!} + \frac{(-3)(-4)(-5)x^3}{3!} + \dots$	Use the expansion formula to write all the required terms.
$= 1 - 3x + \frac{12x^2}{2} - \frac{60x^3}{6} + \dots$	Simplify the expansion.
$= 1 - 3x + 6x^2 - 10x^3 + \dots$	
(b) $\|x\| < 1$ $-1 < x < 1$	State the range for which the expansion is valid.

EXAMPLE 2

- (a) Expand $(1 - 3x)^{-2}$ giving the terms up to and including the x^3 term.

  (b) State the range of values for which this expansion is valid.

SOLUTION

(a) $(1 - 3x)^{-2} = 1 + (-2)(-3x) + \frac{(-2)(-3)(-3x)^2}{2!} + \frac{(-2)(-3)(-4)(-3x)^3}{3!} + \dots$	In this expansion, $(-3x)$ is placed in brackets and both the x and the (-3) must be raised to the power.
$= 1 + 6x + \frac{6 \times 9x^2}{2} + \frac{(-24) \times (-27x^3)}{6} + \dots$	Simplify the expansion, paying particular attention to the negative signs.
$= 1 + 6x + \frac{54x^2}{2} + \frac{648x^3}{6} + \dots$	
$= 1 + 6x + 27x^2 + 108x^3 + \dots$	
(b) $\|3x\| < 1$ $-1 < 3x < 1$ $-\frac{1}{3} < x < \frac{1}{3}$	State the range for which the expansion is valid.

BINOMIAL SERIES $(1 + x)^n$ FOR ANY EXPONENT II

KEY POINTS AND DEFINITIONS

- Examples below consider the case when n is a rational number, that is a fraction.

EXAMPLE 1

- **(a)** Find the binomial expansion of $\sqrt{1 + x}$ giving the first 4 terms of the expansion.

  (b) Use the expansion to find $\sqrt{1.2}$, giving your final answer to three decimal places.

SOLUTION

(a) $\sqrt{1 + x} = (1 + x)^{\frac{1}{2}}$	First write $\sqrt{1 + x}$ in the form $(1 + x)^n$.
$(1 + x)^{\frac{1}{2}} = 1 + \frac{1}{2}x + \dfrac{\left(\frac{1}{2}\right)\left(-\frac{1}{2}\right)}{2!}x^2 + \dfrac{\left(\frac{1}{2}\right)\left(-\frac{1}{2}\right)\left(-\frac{3}{2}\right)}{3!}x^3 + \dots$	Use the formula for the expansion. Take care when working with the fractions.
$= 1 + \frac{1}{2}x + \dfrac{\left(-\frac{1}{4}\right)}{2}x^2 + \dfrac{\left(\frac{3}{8}\right)}{6}x^3 + \dots$	Simplify the expansion.
$= 1 + \frac{1}{2}x - \frac{1}{8}x^2 + \frac{1}{16}x^3 + \dots$	
(b) $x = 0.2$	State the value of x that will give $\sqrt{1.2}$.
$\sqrt{1.2} = 1 + \frac{1}{2} \times 0.2 - \frac{1}{8} \times 0.2^2 + \frac{1}{16} \times 0.2^3 + \dots$	Substitute $x = 0.2$ and calculate the value.
$\approx 1 + 0.1 - 0.005 + 0.0005$	
$= 1.0955 = 1.096$ (to 3 d.p.)	

EXAMPLE 2

- Expand $\sqrt[3]{1 - 2x}$, giving the first four terms. Hence find $\sqrt[3]{0.6}$ to two decimal places.

SOLUTION

$\sqrt[3]{1 - 2x} = (1 - 2x)^{\frac{1}{3}}$	First write in the form $(1 + x)^n$.
$(1 - 2x)^{\frac{1}{3}} = 1 + \frac{1}{3}(-2x) + \dfrac{\left(\frac{1}{3}\right)\left(-\frac{2}{3}\right)}{2!}(-2x)^2 + \dfrac{\left(\frac{1}{3}\right)\left(-\frac{2}{3}\right)\left(-\frac{5}{3}\right)}{3!}(-2x)^3 + \dots$	Use the formula to create the expansion.
$= 1 - \frac{2}{3}x + \dfrac{\left(-\frac{2}{9}\right)}{2} \times 4x^2 + \dfrac{\left(\frac{10}{27}\right)}{6}(-8x^3) + \dots$	Simplify the result, being careful with the signs and fractions.
$= 1 - \frac{2}{3}x - \frac{4}{9}x^2 - \frac{40}{81}x^3 + \dots$	
$x = 0.2$	State the value of x needed to find $\sqrt[3]{0.6}$.
$\sqrt[3]{0.6} \approx 1 - \frac{2}{3} \times 0.2 - \frac{4}{9} \times 0.2^2 - \frac{40}{81} \times 0.2^3 = 0.84$ (to 2 d.p.)	Substitute and calculate the final value.

BINOMIAL SERIES FOR $(a + bx)^n$

KEY POINTS AND DEFINITIONS

- When expanding $(a + bx)^n$, first remember that

  $(a + bx)^n = a^n\left(1 + \dfrac{bx}{a}\right)^n$.

  Then expand $\left(1 + \dfrac{bx}{a}\right)^n$ using the formula for $(1 + x)^n$

  from the formula book and multiply by a^n.

GIVEN FORMULAE ...

$(1 + x)^n = 1 + nx + \dfrac{n(n-1)x^2}{2!} + \dfrac{n(n-1)(n-2)x^3}{3!} + \cdots$

EXAMPLE 1

- (a) Expand $(2 + 3x)^{-2}$, giving the terms up to and including x^3.

  (b) State the range of values of x for which the expansion is valid.

SOLUTION

(a) $(2 + 3x)^{-2} = 2^{-2}\left(1 + \dfrac{3x}{2}\right)^{-2}$	Rewrite the expression so that the bracket is in the form $(1 + kx)^{-2}$.
$= \dfrac{1}{4}\left(1 + (-2)\times\left(\dfrac{3x}{2}\right) + \dfrac{(-2)(-3)}{2!}\left(\dfrac{3x}{2}\right)^2 + \dfrac{(-2)(-3)(-4)}{3!}\left(\dfrac{3x}{2}\right)^3 + \cdots\right)$	Expand using the binomial expansion and remembering that $2^{-2} = \dfrac{1}{4}$.
$= \dfrac{1}{4}\left(1 - 3x + 3\times\dfrac{9x^2}{4} - 4\times\dfrac{27x^3}{8} + \cdots\right)$	Carefully simplify the result.
$= \dfrac{1}{4}\left(1 - 3x + \dfrac{27x^2}{4} - \dfrac{27x^3}{2} + \cdots\right)$	
$= \dfrac{1}{4} - \dfrac{3x}{4} + \dfrac{27x^2}{16} - \dfrac{27x^3}{8} + \cdots$	
(b) $-1 < \dfrac{3x}{2} < 1$	Use $\left|\dfrac{3x}{2}\right| < 1$ to find the range of values.
$-\dfrac{2}{3} < x < \dfrac{2}{3}$	

EXAMPLE 2

- Find the coefficient of x^2 in the expansion of $(5 + 2x)^{-3}$.

SOLUTION

$(5 + 2x)^{-3} = 5^{-3}\left(1 + \dfrac{2x}{5}\right)^{-3}$	Remove the 5 from the bracket and multiply by 5^{-3}.
Coefficient of $x^2 = 5^{-3}\times\dfrac{(-3)(-4)}{2!}\left(\dfrac{2}{5}\right)^2$	Evaluate the coefficient using the standard formula.
$= \dfrac{1}{125}\times 6\times\dfrac{4}{25} = \dfrac{24}{3125}$	

SERIES EXPANSION OF RATIONAL FUNCTIONS

KEY POINTS AND DEFINITIONS

- When asked for the series expansion of a rational function, the first stage is to use partial fractions to convert the rational function into two fractions.

- These fractions can then be expanded using the binomial expansion. Finally the two expansions can be added together.

EXAMPLE

- Find the series expansion for $\dfrac{2x + 1}{x^2 - 5x + 6}$ up to and including the term in x^2 and find the range of values of x for which it is valid.

SOLUTION

$\dfrac{2x + 1}{x^2 - 5x + 6} = \dfrac{2x + 1}{(x - 2)(x - 3)}$	Factorise the denominator.
$= \dfrac{A}{(x - 2)} + \dfrac{B}{(x - 3)}$ $= \dfrac{A(x - 3) + B(x - 2)}{(x - 2)(x - 3)}$	Select the correct partial fractions format and create a common denominator.
$2x + 1 = A(x - 3) + B(x - 2)$	Compare the numerators.
If $x = 3$, $B = 7$ If $x = 2$, $5 = -A$, so that $A = -5$	Substitute values of x to find A and B.
$\dfrac{2x + 1}{x^2 - 5x + 6} = \dfrac{5}{2 - x} - \dfrac{7}{3 - x}$ $= 5(2 - x)^{-1} - 7(3 - x)^{-1}$ $= \dfrac{5}{2}\left(1 - \dfrac{x}{2}\right)^{-1} - \dfrac{7}{3}\left(1 - \dfrac{x}{3}\right)^{-1}$	Rearrange the two fractions to give brackets of the form $\left(1 - \dfrac{x}{k}\right)^n$.
$\left(1 - \dfrac{x}{2}\right)^{-1} = 1 + (-1)\left(-\dfrac{x}{2}\right) + \dfrac{(-1)(-2)}{2!}\left(-\dfrac{x}{2}\right)^2 + \ldots$ $= 1 + \dfrac{x}{2} + \dfrac{x^2}{4} + \ldots$	Use the binomial expansion for the first bracket.
$\left(1 - \dfrac{x}{3}\right)^{-1} = 1 + (-1)\left(-\dfrac{x}{3}\right) + \dfrac{(-1)(-2)}{2!}\left(-\dfrac{x}{3}\right)^2 + \ldots$ $= 1 + \dfrac{x}{3} + \dfrac{x^2}{9} + \ldots$	Repeat for the second bracket.
$\dfrac{2x + 1}{x^2 - 5x + 6} = \dfrac{5}{2}\left(1 + \dfrac{x}{2} + \dfrac{x^2}{4} + \ldots\right) - \dfrac{7}{3}\left(1 + \dfrac{x}{3} + \dfrac{x^2}{9} + \ldots\right)$ $= \dfrac{5}{2} + \dfrac{5x}{4} + \dfrac{5x^2}{8} - \dfrac{7}{3} - \dfrac{7x}{9} - \dfrac{7x^2}{27} + \ldots$ $= \dfrac{1}{6} + \dfrac{17x}{36} + \dfrac{79x^2}{216} + \ldots$	Now combine the two expansions and simplify.
$-1 < \dfrac{x}{2} < 1$ and $-1 < \dfrac{x}{3} < 1$ $-2 < x < 2$ and $-3 < x < 3$ so $-2 < x < 2$	For the expansion to be valid, values of x must satisfy both inequalities.

DOUBLE ANGLE FORMULAE

KEY POINTS AND DEFINITIONS

- Must learn the double angle formulae or be able to derive them quickly from the addition formulae that are listed in the formula book.

> **MUST REMEMBER ...**
>
> $\sin 2A = 2\sin A \cos A$
>
> $\cos 2A = \cos^2 A - \sin^2 A = 2\cos^2 A - 1 = 1 - 2\sin^2 A$
>
> $\tan 2A = \dfrac{2 \tan A}{1 - \tan^2 A}$

EXAMPLE 1

- (a) Show that $\cos(2x) = 1 - 2\sin^2 x$.

- (b) Hence solve the equation $\cos(2x) = \sin x$, giving all the solutions in the range $0 \le x \le 360°$.

SOLUTION

(a) $\cos(2x) = \cos(x + x)$	Use the addition formula:
$\quad = \cos x \cos x - \sin x \sin x$	$\cos(A + B) = \cos A \cos B - \sin A \sin B$
$\quad = \cos^2 x - \sin^2 x$	with $A = B = x$.
$\quad = 1 - \sin^2 x - \sin^2 x$	Using $\sin^2 x + \cos^2 x = 1$, substitute for $\cos^2 x$.
$\quad = 1 - 2\sin^2 x$	
(b) $\qquad \cos(2x) = \sin x$	Replace the $\cos(2x)$ term by $1 - 2\sin^2 x$ and simplify.
$\qquad 1 - 2\sin^2 x = \sin x$	
$2\sin^2 x + \sin x - 1 = 0$	
$(2\sin x - 1)(\sin x + 1) = 0$	Solve the quadratic equation and find the possible values of $\sin x$.
$\sin x = \dfrac{1}{2}$ or $\sin x = -1$	
$x = \sin^{-1}\left(\dfrac{1}{2}\right) = 30°$ or $x = 180 - 30 = 150°$	Find the values of x for which $\sin x = \dfrac{1}{2}$.
$x = \sin^{-1}(-1) = 270°$	Find the value of x for which $\sin x = -1$.
$x = 30°$ or $150°$ or $270°$	List all the solutions of the equation.

EXAMPLE 2

- Show that $\tan 2A = \dfrac{2 \tan A}{1 - \tan^2 A}$.

SOLUTION

$\tan(2A) = \tan(A + A)$	Use the formula from the book,
$\quad = \dfrac{\tan A + \tan A}{1 - \tan A \times \tan A} = \dfrac{2 \tan A}{1 - \tan^2 A}$	$\tan(A + B) = \dfrac{\tan A + \tan B}{1 - \tan A \tan B}$ with A = B.

TRIGONOMETRY – COMPOUND ANGLE FORMULAE

KEY POINTS AND DEFINITIONS

- The compound angle formulae are of the form $\sin(A \pm B)$ and also exist for cos and tan. These formulae are listed in the formula book and need to be referred to quickly.

GIVEN FORMULAE ...

$$\sin(A \pm B) = \sin A \cos B \pm \cos A \sin B$$

$$\cos(A \pm B) = \cos A \cos B \mp \sin A \sin B$$

$$\tan(A \pm B) = \frac{\tan A \pm \tan B}{1 \mp \tan A \tan B}$$

Use the $\pm$ and $\mp$ signs carefully. Always use the top symbol in the formula or the bottom symbol, for example $\cos(A + B) = \cos A \cos B - \sin A \sin B$.

EXAMPLE 1

- Prove that $\sin(x + 90°) = \cos x$.

SOLUTION

$\sin(x + 90°) = \sin x \cos 90° + \cos x \sin 90°$	Use the $\sin(A + B)$ formula.
$= \sin x \times 0 + \cos x \times 1$	$\cos 90° = 0$ and $\sin 90° = 1$.
$= \cos x$	

EXAMPLE 2

- Prove that $\tan(x - 45°) = \dfrac{\tan x - 1}{1 + \tan x}$

SOLUTION

$\tan(x - 45°) = \dfrac{\tan x - \tan 45°}{1 + \tan x \tan 45°}$	Use the $\tan(A - B)$ formula.
$= \dfrac{\tan x - 1}{1 + \tan x \times 1} = \dfrac{\tan x - 1}{1 + \tan x}.$	$\tan 45° = 1$.

EXAMPLE 2

- **(a)** Prove that $\cos x + \cos(180° - x) = 0$ and $\sin x - \sin(180° - x) = 0$.

- **(b)** Hence prove that $\sin(x + 30°) + \sin(x - 150°) = 0$.

SOLUTION

(a) $\cos x + \cos(180° - x) = \cos x + \cos 180° \cos x + \sin 180° \sin x$	Use the $\cos(A - B)$ formula. Remember that $\cos 180° = -1$.
$= \cos x - \cos x + 0$	
$= 0$	
$\sin x - \sin(180° - x) = \sin x - (\sin 180° \cos x - \cos 180° \sin x)$	Use the $\sin(A - B)$ formula. Remember that $\sin 180° = 0$.
$= \sin x - 0 - \sin x$	
$= 0$	
(b) $\sin(x + 30°) + \sin(x - 150°)$	Use the $\sin(A + B)$ and $\sin(A - B)$ formulae. Then use the two results from (a) above.
$= \sin x \cos 30° + \cos x \sin 30° + \sin x \cos 150° - \cos x \sin 150°$	
$= \sin x(\cos 30° + \cos 150°) + \cos x(\sin 30° - \sin 150°)$	
$= \sin x(\cos 30° + \cos(180° - 30°)) + \cos x(\sin 30° - \sin(180° - 30°))$	
$= \sin x \times 0 + \cos x \times 0$	
$= 0$	

AQA C4

Edexcel C3

OCR C3

OCR(MEI) C4

WJEC C4

TRIGONOMETRIC IDENTITIES I

AQA C4

Edexcel C3

OCR C3

OCR(MEI) C4

WJEC C4

KEY POINTS AND DEFINITIONS

- Many trigonometric identities can be proved by using the trigonometric formulae listed below and to the right. Others, for example $1 + \tan^2 x = \sec^2 x$ and the double angle formulae, can be derived from those listed.

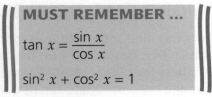

MUST REMEMBER ...

$$\tan x = \frac{\sin x}{\cos x}$$

$$\sin^2 x + \cos^2 x = 1$$

GIVEN FORMULAE ...

$$\sin (A \pm B) = \sin A \cos B \pm \cos A \sin B$$

$$\cos (A \pm B) = \cos A \cos B \mp \sin A \sin B$$

$$\tan (A \pm B) = \frac{\tan A \pm \tan B}{1 \mp \tan A \tan B}$$

EXAMPLE 1

- Prove that $\dfrac{\sin(x - y)}{\cos x \cos y} = \tan x - \tan y$.

SOLUTION

$\dfrac{\sin(x - y)}{\cos x \cos y} = \dfrac{\sin x \cos y - \cos x \sin y}{\cos x \cos y}$	Expand the numerator using the formula for $\sin (A - B)$.
$= \dfrac{\sin x \cos y}{\cos x \cos y} - \dfrac{\cos x \sin y}{\cos x \cos y}$ $= \dfrac{\sin x}{\cos x} - \dfrac{\sin y}{\cos y}$	Split the expression into two fractions and cancel each one down.
$= \tan x - \tan y$	Use $\tan x = \dfrac{\sin x}{\cos x}$ to complete the argument.

EXAMPLE 2

- Prove that $\dfrac{1 + \sin (2x) + \cos (2x)}{1 + \sin (2x) - \cos (2x)} = \cot x$.

SOLUTION

$\dfrac{1 + \sin (2x) + \cos (2x)}{1 + \sin (2x) - \cos (2x)} = \dfrac{1 + 2\sin x \cos x + \cos^2 x - \sin^2 x}{1 + 2\sin x \cos x - \cos^2 x + \sin^2 x}$	Use the formulae for $\sin (2x)$ and $\cos (2x)$.
$= \dfrac{1 + 2\sin x \cos x + \cos^2 x - (1 - \cos^2 x)}{1 + 2\sin x \cos x - (1 - \sin^2 x) + \sin^2 x}$ $= \dfrac{1 + 2\sin x \cos x - 1 + 2\cos^2 x}{1 + 2\sin x \cos x - 1 + 2\sin^2 x}$ $= \dfrac{2\cos^2 x + 2\sin x \cos x}{2\sin^2 x + 2\sin x \cos x}$	Eliminate $\sin^2 x$ from the numerator using $\sin^2 x = 1 - \cos^2 x$ and $\cos^2 x$ by using $\cos^2 x = 1 - \sin^2 x$.
$= \dfrac{\cos x(\cos x + \sin x)}{\sin x(\cos x + \sin x)}$ $= \dfrac{\cos x}{\sin x}$	Divide numerator and denominator by 2. Then factorise and simplify.
$= \dfrac{1}{\tan x}$ $= \cot x$	Finally use $\cot x = \dfrac{1}{\tan x}$ to finish.

TRIGONOMETRIC IDENTITIES II

KEY POINTS AND DEFINITIONS

- This is a further example of how trigonometric identities can be used to rearrange equations and help to obtain solutions to equations.

EXAMPLE

- **(a)** Show that $\tan(3x) = \dfrac{3\tan x - \tan^3 x}{1 - 3\tan^2 x}$.

  (b) Hence solve the equation $\tan^3 x - 3\tan^2 x - 3\tan x + 1 = 0$.

SOLUTION

(a) $\tan(3x) = \tan(2x + x)$ $= \dfrac{\tan(2x) + \tan x}{1 - \tan(2x)\tan x}$	Use the formula for $\tan(A + B)$ with $A = 2x$ and $B = x$.
$= \dfrac{\dfrac{\tan x + \tan x}{1 - \tan^2 x} + \tan x}{1 - \dfrac{\tan x + \tan x}{1 - \tan^2 x}\tan x}$ $= \dfrac{\dfrac{2\tan x}{1 - \tan^2 x} + \tan x}{1 - \dfrac{2\tan x}{1 - \tan^2 x}\tan x}$	Use the formula for $\tan(2x)$ and begin to simplify the expression.
$= \dfrac{2\tan x + \tan x(1 - \tan^2 x)}{1 - \tan^2 x - 2\tan^2 x}$ $= \dfrac{2\tan x + \tan x - \tan^3 x}{1 - 3\tan^2 x}$ $= \dfrac{3\tan x - \tan^3 x}{1 - 3\tan^2 x}$	Multiply the numerator and the denominator by $(1 - \tan^2 x)$ and simplify to obtain the required result.
(b) $\tan^3 x - 3\tan^2 x - 3\tan x + 1 = 0$ $3\tan x - \tan^3 x = 1 - 3\tan^2 x$ $\dfrac{3\tan x - \tan^3 x}{1 - 3\tan^2 x} = 1$	The equation contains terms that are found in the identity considered above. Use this to form an equation in which the identity can be used.
$\tan(3x) = 1$	Replace the expression on the left hand side by $\tan(3x)$.
$3x = \dfrac{\pi}{4}$ or $3x = \dfrac{\pi}{4} + \pi = \dfrac{5\pi}{4}$ or $3x = \dfrac{\pi}{4} + 2\pi = \dfrac{9\pi}{4}$ or $3x = \dfrac{\pi}{4} + 3\pi = \dfrac{13\pi}{4}$ or $3x = \dfrac{\pi}{4} + 4\pi = \dfrac{17\pi}{4}$ or $3x = \dfrac{\pi}{4} + 5\pi = \dfrac{21\pi}{4}$	Write down six solutions for $3x$.
$x = \dfrac{\pi}{12}$ or $x = \dfrac{5\pi}{12}$ or $x = \dfrac{3\pi}{4}$ or $x = \dfrac{13\pi}{12}$ or $x = \dfrac{17\pi}{12}$ or $x = \dfrac{7\pi}{4}$	Divide by 3 to find the six values for x.

AQA C4
Edexcel C3
OCR C3
OCR(MEI) C4
WJEC C4

USE OF $r\cos(\theta + \alpha)$

KEY POINTS AND DEFINITIONS

- It is possible to write $a\cos\theta - b\sin\theta$ in the form $r\cos(\theta + \alpha)$.

- Using the addition formula:

$$r\cos(\theta + \alpha) = r(\cos\theta\cos\alpha - \sin\theta\sin\alpha)$$

$$= r\cos\alpha\cos\theta - r\sin\alpha\sin\theta$$

$$= a\cos\theta - b\sin\theta$$

where $a = r\cos\alpha$ and $b = r\sin\alpha$.

- To find r:

$$a^2 + b^2 = r^2\cos^2\alpha + r^2\sin^2\alpha = r^2(\cos^2\alpha + \sin^2\alpha) = r^2, \text{ so } r = \sqrt{a^2 + b^2}.$$

- To find α:

$$\frac{b}{a} = \frac{r\sin\alpha}{r\cos\alpha} = \tan\alpha, \text{ so } \alpha = \tan^{-1}\left(\frac{b}{a}\right).$$

EXAMPLE

- **(a)** Write $12\cos x - 5\sin x$ in the form $r\cos(x + \alpha)$.

- **(b)** Hence solve the equation $12\cos x - 5\sin x = 4$, giving the solutions in the range $0 \le x \le 360°$.

SOLUTION

(a) $r\cos(x + \alpha) = r(\cos x\cos\alpha - \sin x\sin\alpha)$	Use the formula for $\cos(A + B)$ from the formula book as the first step.
$r\cos\alpha = 12$ and $r\sin\alpha = 5$	Write down the values of $r\cos\alpha$ and $r\sin\alpha$.
$\tan\alpha = \dfrac{r\sin\alpha}{r\cos\alpha} = \dfrac{5}{12}$ $\alpha = 22.6°$	Find α by finding the value of $\tan\alpha$.
$r^2 = (r\cos\alpha)^2 + (r\sin\alpha)^2 = 12^2 + 5^2$ $r = \sqrt{169} = 13$	Find r, using the identity $\cos^2\alpha + \sin^2\alpha = 1$.
$12\cos x - 5\sin x = 13\cos(x + 22.6°)$	Write the expression in the new form.
(b) $12\cos x - 5\sin x = 4$ $13\cos(x + 22.6°) = 4$	Use the result from (a) to rewrite the equation.
$\cos(x + 22.6°) = \dfrac{4}{13}$	Find the value of $\cos\alpha$.
$x + 22.6 = 72.1$ or $x + 22.6 = 360 - 72.1 = 287.9$	Find the two possible values of $x + 22.6$.
$x = 49.5°$ or $x = 265.3°$	Subtract 22.6 from both values to give the two solutions.

USE OF $r\sin(\theta + \alpha)$

KEY POINTS AND DEFINITIONS

- It is possible to write $a\cos\theta + b\sin\theta$ in the form $r\sin(\theta + \alpha)$.
- Using the addition formula:

$$r\sin(\theta + \alpha) = r(\cos\theta\sin\alpha + \sin\theta\cos\alpha)$$

$$= r\sin\alpha\cos\theta + r\cos\alpha\sin\theta$$

$$= a\cos\theta + b\sin\theta$$

where $a = r\sin\alpha$ and $b = r\cos\alpha$.

- To find r:

$$a^2 + b^2 = r^2\sin^2\alpha + r^2\cos^2\alpha = r^2(\sin^2\alpha + \cos^2\alpha) = r^2, \text{ so } r = \sqrt{a^2 + b^2}.$$

- To find α:

$$\frac{a}{b} = \frac{r\sin\alpha}{r\cos\alpha} = \tan\alpha, \text{ so } \alpha = \tan^{-1}\left(\frac{a}{b}\right).$$

EXAMPLE

- **(a)** Write $\cos x + \sqrt{3}\sin x$ in the form $r\sin(x + \alpha)$.

  (b) Hence solve the equation $\cos x + \sqrt{3}\sin x = \frac{1}{2}$,

  giving the solutions in the range $0 \leq x \leq 360°$.

SOLUTION

(a) $r\sin(x + \alpha) = r\sin\alpha\cos x + r\cos\alpha\sin x$	Use the formula for $\sin(A + B)$ from the formula book as the first step.
$r\sin\alpha = 1$ and $r\cos\alpha = \sqrt{3}$	Write down the values of $r\sin\alpha$ and $r\cos\alpha$.
$\tan\alpha = \dfrac{r\sin\alpha}{r\cos\alpha} = \dfrac{1}{\sqrt{3}}$ $\alpha = 30°$	Find α by finding the value of $\tan\alpha$.
$r^2 = (r\cos\alpha)^2 + (r\sin\alpha)^2 = 1 + 3$ $r = \sqrt{4} = 2$	Find r, using the identity $\cos^2\alpha + \sin^2\alpha = 1$.
$\cos x + \sqrt{3}\sin x = 2\sin(x + 30°)$	Write the expression in the new form.
(b) $\cos x - \sqrt{3}\sin x = \dfrac{1}{2}$ $2\sin(x + 30) = \dfrac{1}{2}$	Use the result from (a) to rewrite the equation.
$\sin(x + 30) = \dfrac{1}{4}$	Find the value of $\sin(x + 30)$.
$x + 30 = 14.5$ or $x + 30 = 180 - 14.5 = 165.5$ or $x + 30 = 360 + 14.5 = 374.5$	Find the two possible values of $x + 30$.
$x = 135.5°$ or $x = 344.5°$	Subtract 30 from the two values which are greater than 30 to give the two solutions.

AQA C4 · Edexcel C3 · OCR C3 · OCR(MEI) C4 · WJEC C4

USE OF TRIGONOMETRIC IDENTITIES IN INTEGRATION I

KEY POINTS AND DEFINITIONS

- Trigonometric identities can be used to rearrange integrals so that they are in a form that can be easily integrated. Often they will be used to reduce an integral to a single trigonometric term.

EXAMPLE 1

- (a) Show that $\sin^2 x = \frac{1}{2}(1 - \cos(2x))$.

  (b) Hence evaluate $\int_0^{\pi} \sin^2 x \, dx$.

SOLUTION

(a) $\cos(2x) = \cos(x + x)$ $\qquad = \cos x \cos x - \sin x \sin x$ $\qquad = \cos^2 x - \sin^2 x$	Start with $\cos(2x)$ and rearrange using the formula for $\cos(A + B)$.
$\cos(2x) = 1 - \sin^2 x - \sin^2 x$ $\qquad = 1 - 2\sin^2 x$	Use the identity $\sin^2 x + \cos^2 x = 1$.
$2\sin^2 x = 1 - \cos(2x)$ $\sin^2 x = \frac{1}{2}(1 - \cos(2x))$	Make $\sin^2 x$ the subject of the expression.
(b) $\int_0^{\pi} \sin^2 x \, dx = \int_0^{\pi} \frac{1}{2}(1 - \cos(2x)) dx$ $\qquad = \frac{1}{2}\int_0^{\pi} (1 - \cos(2x)) dx$	Use the result from (a) to simplify the integral.
$\qquad = \frac{1}{2}\left[x - \frac{1}{2}\sin(2x)\right]_0^{\pi}$ $\qquad = \frac{1}{2}\left(\left(\pi - \frac{1}{2}\sin(2\pi)\right) - \left(0 - \frac{1}{2}\sin(0)\right)\right)$ $\qquad = \frac{\pi}{2}$	Integrate and then substitute the limits to find the value of the integral.

EXAMPLE 2

- Use the formula for $\sin(2x)$ to show that $\int \sin x \cos x \, dx = -\frac{1}{4}\cos(2x) + c$.

SOLUTION

$\sin(2x) = 2\sin x \cos x$ $\sin x \cos x = \frac{1}{2}\sin(2x)$	Quote or derive the formula for $\sin(2x)$.
$\int \sin x \cos x \, dx = \int \frac{1}{2}\sin(2x) dx$ $\qquad = -\frac{1}{4}\cos(2x) + c$	Use the formula to rearrange the integral and then integrate, including a constant of integration.

USE OF TRIGONOMETRIC IDENTITIES IN INTEGRATION II

KEY POINTS AND DEFINITIONS

- This is a further example of using trigonometric identities to rearrange integrals so that they are in a form that can be easily integrated.

EXAMPLE

- **(a)** Show that $\cos(3x) = 4\cos^3 x - 3\cos x$.

  (b) Hence evaluate $\int_0^{\frac{\pi}{2}} \cos^3 x\,dx$.

SOLUTION

(a) $\cos(3x) = \cos(2x + x)$ $= \cos(2x)\cos x - \sin(2x)\sin x$	Start with $\cos(3x)$ and rearrange using the formula for $\cos(A + B)$.
$= (\cos^2 x - \sin^2 x)\cos x - 2\sin x\cos x\sin x$ $= \cos^3 x - \sin^2 x\cos x - 2\sin^2 x\cos x$ $= \cos^3 x - 3\sin^2 x\cos x$	Use $\cos(2x) = \cos^2 x - \sin^2 x$ and $\sin(2x) = 2\sin x\cos x$ to expand further.
$= \cos^3 x - 3(1 - \cos^2 x)\cos x$ $= \cos^3 x - 3\cos x + 3\cos^3 x$ $= 4\cos^3 x - 3\cos x$	Now use $\sin^2 x = 1 - \cos^2 x$ to eliminate the $\sin x$ terms and give the required result.
(b) $\cos(3x) = 4\cos^3 x - 3\cos x$ $4\cos^3 x = \cos(3x) + 3\cos x$ $\cos^3 x = \frac{1}{4}(\cos(3x) + 3\cos x)$	Make $\cos^3 x$ the subject of the expression from (a).
$\int_0^{\frac{\pi}{2}} \cos^3 x\,dx = \int_0^{\frac{\pi}{2}} \frac{1}{4}(\cos(3x) + 3\cos x)dx$	Use this expression for $\cos^3 x$ to simplify the integral.
$= \frac{1}{4}\left[\frac{1}{3}\sin(3x) + 3\sin x\right]_0^{\frac{\pi}{2}}$ $= \frac{1}{4}\left(\left(\frac{1}{3}\sin\left(\frac{3\pi}{2}\right) + 3\sin\left(\frac{\pi}{2}\right)\right) - \left(\frac{1}{3}\sin 0 + 3\sin 0\right)\right)$	Integrate and substitute the limits of integration.
$= \frac{1}{4}\left(-\frac{1}{3} + 3\right)$ $= \frac{2}{3}$	$\sin\left(\frac{3\pi}{2}\right) = -1$ and $\sin\left(\frac{\pi}{2}\right) = 1$.

EXPONENTIAL GROWTH AND DECAY

KEY POINTS AND DEFINITIONS

- A quantity growing exponentially can be modelled by a function $f(t) = ka^t$ where k and a are constants.

- A quantity decaying exponentially can be modelled by a function $f(t) = ka^{-t}$ where k and a are constants and a is called the base of the exponential model.

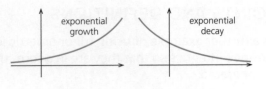

EXAMPLE 1

- A radioactive substance has a half-life of one week, i.e. every week it decays by half of its value at the beginning of the week. Its initial level of radioactivity is 20.

  (a) Complete the following table of values, showing levels of radioactivity over a five-week period.

Time (weeks)	0	1	2	3	4	5
Radioactivity	20	10				

  (b) Draw a graph of quantity of radioactivity against time in weeks.

  (c) Use your graph to estimate:
  (i) the amount of radioactivity after 10 days;
  (ii) the time it takes for the radioactivity to reach 10% of its initial value.

  (d) Find a formula between the quantity of radioactivity and time.

SOLUTION

(a)
Time (weeks)	0	1	2	3	4	5
Radioactivity	20	10	5	2.5	1.25	0.625

(b)

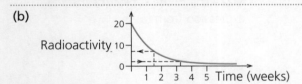

The graph needs to be drawn carefully so that it can be used in part (c).

(c) (i) The amount of radioactivity after 10 days = 7.5

   (ii) The time it takes for the radioactivity to reach 10% of its initial value is between 3 and $3\frac{1}{2}$ weeks

(d) Level of radioactivity = 20×2^{-n} where n is the number of weeks

2^{-n} could also be written as 0.5^n.

EXAMPLE 2

- A sum of £1500 is invested in a building society that pays 5.5% compound interest per annum. Find the number of years required for the value of the investment to double.

SOLUTION

$A = 1500 \times 1.055^n$
where A is the amount of the investment after n years.

First form an equation to describe the situation.

When $A = 3000$

$1500 \times 1.055^n = 3000$

$1.055^n = \dfrac{3000}{1500} = 2$

To solve, simplify and take logs of both sides.

$\log 1.055^n = \log 2 \implies n = \dfrac{\log(2)}{\log(1.055)} = 12.95$

Use the rule $\log b^a = a\log b$.

After 13 years the investment will have doubled.

Must remember to round up to the next full year as the answer.

MODELLING WITH EXPONENTIAL FUNCTIONS

KEY POINTS AND DEFINITIONS

- When modelling with exponential functions, the mathematical constant $e = 2.7182818$ (to 8 significant figures) is often chosen as the base.

EXAMPLE 1

- In a laboratory experiment, it is found that bacteria are growing rapidly according to the law $N = N_0 e^{kt}$, where N is the number of bacteria present at time t hours and N_0 and k are constants.

  (a) Explain the significance of N_0.

  (b) If the number of bacteria grows from 100000 to 250000 in the first four hours, how many bacteria do you predict there will be after 10 hours?

SOLUTION

(a) $N = N_0 e^{kt}$ N_0 is the initial number of bacteria	Must remember that when $t = 0$, $e^0 = 1$ and then $N = N_0$.
(b) $t = 0$, $N = 100000 = N_0$ $t = 4$, $N = 250000 = 100000\,e^{4k}$ $\quad e^{4k} = 2.5$ $\quad\quad k = \dfrac{1}{4}\ln 2.5 = 0.2291$ When $t = 10$, $N = 100000\,e^{10k} = 988212$	First find the values of N_0 and k. Now substitute $t = 10$ to find N after 10 hours.

EXAMPLE 2

- At t minutes after an oven is switched on its temperature $T°C$ is given by

  $T = 180 - 160e^{-0.2t}$.

  (a) State the initial temperature of the oven when it was switched on.

  (b) State the cooking temperature reached after a long time.

  (c) Find the temperature of the oven after 10 minutes.

  (d) Find the rate at which the temperature is increasing at the instant it reaches 100°C.

SOLUTION

(a) $T(0) = 180 - 160 = 20$ The initial oven temperature is 20°C	Must remember the value of e^{-kt} when $t = 0$ and when t is very large.
(b) As $t \to \infty$, $e^{-0.2t} \to 0$ so $T \to 180$ The oven will eventually reach 180°C	
(c) $T(10) = 180 - 160\,e^{-0.2 \times 10} = 158.3°C$	Find T when $t = 10$.
(d) The rate of increase of temperature $= \dfrac{dT}{dt}$ $\dfrac{dT}{dt} = -160 \times (-0.2)e^{-0.2t} = 32e^{-0.2t}$ When $T = 100$, $180 - 160e^{-0.2t} = 100$ $\quad\quad 160e^{-0.2t} = 80$ $\quad\quad\quad e^{-0.2t} = 0.5$ When $T = 100$, $\dfrac{dT}{dt} = 32 \times 0.5 = 16°C$ per minute	Take care with the signs in calculations like this. There is no need to actually solve for t.

FORMING DIFFERENTIAL EQUATIONS I

KEY POINTS AND DEFINITIONS

- Many real life situations involve growth and decay processes which are represented by models that involve rates of change, i.e. derivatives. Equations involving derivatives are called differential equations.

- A first order differential equation only involves a first derivative.

  The general form of a first order differential equation is $\frac{dy}{dx} = f(x, y)$.

EXAMPLE 1

- A radioactive isotope decays in such a way that the rate of change of the number N of radioactive atoms present after t days is proportional to N. Write down a differential equation relating N and t.

SOLUTION

$\frac{dN}{dt} = -kN$, where k is a constant	As the number of atoms is decreasing and is proportional to N, the rate of change is proportional to $-N$.

EXAMPLE 2

- When a can of cider is taken from the fridge, its temperature is 1°C. The cider warms up so that the rate of change of temperature T°C after t seconds is proportional to T. The room temperature is 20°C.

  (a) Model this situation as an initial value problem, i.e. a differential equation and an initial condition.

  (b) What can you deduce from the information about room temperature? Write this as a mathematical statement.

SOLUTION

(a) $\frac{dT}{dt} = kT$ with $T(0) = 1$	The rate of change of T is positive. The initial temperature is 1°C.

(b) After a long time, the cider reaches room temperature.

As $t \to \infty$, $T \to 20$

EXAMPLE 3

- A rectangular tank has a height of 100 cm and was initially full of oil. A leak was discovered from a hole in the base of the tank. When the leak is found, the tank is three-quarters full and the level of oil is dripping out at a rate of 0.5 cm per minute.

In modelling this situation, it is assumed that when the depth of oil remaining in the tank is h cm, the rate at which the level is dropping is proportional to $\sqrt{h}$. Formulate a differential equation to model this situation.

SOLUTION

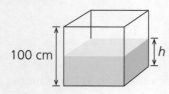
100 cm

Rate at which level is dropping $\frac{dh}{dt} \propto -\sqrt{h}$, i.e. $\frac{dh}{dt} = -k\sqrt{h}$	The rate of change of h is negative as h is decreasing.
When $h = 75$ cm, $\frac{dh}{dt} = -k\sqrt{75} = -0.5$	Find k.
$k = \dfrac{1}{2\sqrt{75}}$ $\frac{dh}{dt} = -\dfrac{1}{2\sqrt{75}}\sqrt{h}$ when $t = 0$, $h = 100$	State the differential equation with initial conditions.

SEPARATION OF VARIABLES I

SEPARATION OF VARIABLES I

KEY POINTS AND DEFINITIONS

- The method of separation of variables can be used to solve first order differential equations of the form
$\frac{dy}{dx} = f(x, y)$ if $f(x, y) = u(x) \times v(y)$.
- The method then gives $\int \frac{1}{v(y)} dy = \int u(x) dx$.

EXAMPLE 1

- The differential equation $\frac{dN}{dt} = -kN$, given that

$N = 70$ when $t = 0$ and $N = 3$ when $t = 8$, models a decaying process.

(a) Solve the equation, expressing N as a function of t.

(b) Sketch a graph showing how N varies with t.

SOLUTION

(a) $\int \frac{1}{N} dN = -\int k dt$ | Separate the variables by dividing each side by N.

$\ln N = -kt + c$ | Integrate both sides.

$t = 0$, $N = 70 \Rightarrow c = \ln 70$ | The conditions at $t = 0$ and $t = 8$ are used to find c and k.

$\ln N = -kt + \ln 70$

$t = 8$, $N = 3 \Rightarrow \ln 3 = -8k + \ln 70$

$k = \frac{1}{8} \ln \frac{70}{3} = 0.3937$

$\ln N - \ln 70 = -kt = -0.3937t$

$N = 70\, e^{-0.3937t}$ | Must remember that $\ln b - \ln a = \ln \frac{b}{a}$.

(b)

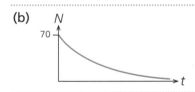

EXAMPLE 2

- Solve the differential equation

$x^2 \frac{dy}{dx} = y + 1$, given that $y(1) = 0$.

Write your answer in the form $y = f(x)$.

Find the value of y when x becomes very large.

SOLUTION

$\int \frac{1}{y + 1} dy = \int \frac{1}{x^2} dx$ | Separate the variables by dividing each side by $y+1$ and x^2.

$\ln |y + 1| = -\frac{1}{x} + c$ | Integrate both sides.

When $x = 1$, $y = 0 \Rightarrow \ln 1 = -1 + c \Rightarrow c = 1$

$\ln |y + 1| = -\frac{1}{x} + 1$

$y + 1 = e^{1 - \frac{1}{x}}$

As x increases, $e^{1 - \frac{1}{x}} \to e^1$, so that $y \to -1 + e$ | As $x \to \infty$, $\frac{1}{x} \to 0$.

SEPARATION OF VARIABLES II

KEY POINTS AND DEFINITIONS

- The method of separation of variables often requires the use of partial fractions and logarithmic functions.

MUST REMEMBER ...

$$\int \frac{1}{a + bx}\,dx = \frac{1}{b}\ln |a + bx|$$

EXAMPLE 1

- The acceleration of a parachutist dropping from a helicopter is given by the formula $\frac{dv}{dt} = 10 - 3v$, where v is the speed of the parachutist vertically downwards at time t. Initially, $v = 0$ when $t = 0$.

  (a) Solve the differential equation to find the speed as a function of time.

  (b) What is the limiting speed of the parachutist?

SOLUTION

(a) $\int \frac{1}{10 - 3v}\,dv = \int dt \Rightarrow -\frac{1}{3}\ln(10 - 3v) = t + c$	Separate the variables and integrate.
$t = 0, v = 0 \Rightarrow -\frac{1}{3}\ln 10 = c$	Use initial conditions to find c.
$-\frac{1}{3}\ln(10 - 3v) = t - \frac{1}{3}\ln 10$ $\ln \frac{10 - 3v}{10} = -3t \Rightarrow \frac{10 - 3v}{10} = e^{-3t} \Rightarrow v = \frac{10 - 10e^{-3t}}{3}$	Rearrange the equation to make v the subject.
(b) As t increases, $v \to \frac{10}{3}$ ms^{-1}	As $t \to \infty$, $e^{-3t} \to 0$.

EXAMPLE 2

- (a) Express $\frac{5 - x}{(x - 2)(x + 1)}$ in partial fractions.

  (b) Given that $y = 2$ at $x = 3$, use your answer to part (a) to find the solution of the differential equation

  $$\frac{dy}{dx} = \frac{y(5 - x)}{(x - 2)(x + 1)}, \quad x > 2.$$

  Write your answer in the form $y = f(x)$.

SOLUTION

(a) $\frac{5 - x}{(x - 2)(x + 1)} = \frac{A}{x - 2} + \frac{B}{x + 1}$ $5 - x = A(x + 1) + B(x - 2)$	Express as partial fractions.
When $x = 2$: $3 = 3A \Rightarrow A = 1$ When $x = -1$: $6 = -3B \Rightarrow B = -2$ $\frac{5 - x}{(x - 2)(x + 1)} = \frac{1}{x - 2} - \frac{2}{x + 1}$	Find A and B.
(b) $\frac{dy}{dx} = \frac{y(5 - x)}{(x - 2)(x + 1)}$ $\int \frac{1}{y}\,dy = \int \frac{5 - x}{(x - 2)(x + 1)}\,dx = \int \left(\frac{1}{x - 2} - \frac{2}{x + 1}\right)dx$ $\ln y = \ln(x - 2) - 2\ln(x + 1) + c$	Separate the variables, then integrate.
When $x = 3$, $y = 2 \Rightarrow \ln 2 = \ln 1 - 2\ln 4 + c$ $c = 5\ln 2$	Must remember $\ln a^n = n\ln a$.
$\ln y = \ln(x - 2) - 2\ln(x + 1) + 5\ln 2$ $= \ln(2^5 \times (x - 2) \times (x + 1)^{-2})$	Must remember $\ln a + \ln b = \ln ab$.
$y = \frac{32(x - 2)}{(x + 1)^2}$	

FORMING DIFFERENTIAL EQUATIONS II

KEY POINTS AND DEFINITIONS

- Differential equations may also occur in mathematical problems such as finding the equation of a curve given the equation of its slope.

- The general solution of a first order differential equation contains one unknown constant and represents a family of solution curves.

- A particular solution is one member of the family of solutions.

EXAMPLE 1

- The tangent to a curve at any point (x, y) has slope inversely proportional to x^2. The curve passes through two points $(1, 1)$ and $(2, 3)$. Find the equation of the curve.

SOLUTION

$\dfrac{dy}{dx} \propto \dfrac{1}{x^2} \Rightarrow \dfrac{dy}{dx} = \dfrac{a}{x^2}$ $$\int dy = \int \frac{a}{x^2}dx$$ $$y = -\frac{a}{x} + c$$	For this differential equation, just integrate each side. Must remember to include a constant of integration. This is the general solution.
When $x = 1$, $y = 1 \Rightarrow 1 = -a + c$ When $x = 2$, $y = 3 \Rightarrow 3 = -\dfrac{a}{2} + c$ Solving for a and c gives $a = 4$ and $c = 5$.	Use the given coordinates on the curve to obtain simultaneous equations in a and c.
The equation of the curve is $y = \dfrac{-4}{x} + 5$	This is the particular solution.

EXAMPLE 2

- A curve passing through the point $(3, 0)$ has gradient function $\dfrac{y + 1}{x^2 - 1}$ $(x > 1, y > -1)$.

Find the equation of the curve and hence sketch the particular solution.

SOLUTION

$$\frac{dy}{dx} = \frac{y + 1}{x^2 - 1}$$	Form the differential equation and use the method of separation of variables to produce two integrals.
$$\int \frac{1}{y + 1} dy = \int \frac{1}{x^2 - 1} dx$$ $$\int \frac{1}{y + 1} dy = \int \left(\frac{1}{2(x - 1)} - \frac{1}{2(x + 1)}\right)dx$$ $$\ln (y + 1) = \frac{1}{2}\ln (x - 1) - \frac{1}{2}\ln (x + 1) + c$$	For the right hand side, use partial fractions.
When $x = 3$, $y = 0$, $\Rightarrow \ln 1 = \dfrac{1}{2}\ln 2 - \dfrac{1}{2}\ln 4 + c$ $c = \dfrac{1}{2}\ln \dfrac{4}{2} = \dfrac{1}{2}\ln 2$ $\ln (y + 1) = \dfrac{1}{2}\ln (x - 1) - \dfrac{1}{2}\ln (x + 1) + \dfrac{1}{2}\ln 2$ $y + 1 = \sqrt{\left(\dfrac{2(x - 1)}{x + 1}\right)}$	Find c to obtain the particular solution. Solve for y.

IMPLICIT DIFFERENTIATION

KEY POINTS AND DEFINITIONS

- Implicit differentiation is used for differentiating expressions like $x^2 + 2xy + y^2 = 9$, which are not in the form $y = f(x)$.

- When using implicit differentiation, differentiate each term with respect to x and then make $\frac{dy}{dx}$ the subject of the expression.

- When differentiating terms that are functions of y, apply the chain rule.

- If differentiating f(y) with respect to x, the result $\frac{df}{dx} = \frac{df}{dy} \times \frac{dy}{dx}$ is obtained. For example, differentiating y^5 gives $5y^4 \frac{dy}{dx}$.

> **MUST REMEMBER ...**
>
> $\frac{d}{dx} f(y) = \frac{df}{dy} \times \frac{dy}{dx}$

EXAMPLE 1

- If $x^2 + y^2 = 7$, find $\frac{dy}{dx}$.

SOLUTION

$2x + 2y \frac{dy}{dx} = 0$	First differentiate each term with respect to x. Remember that $\frac{d}{dx}(y^2) = 2y\frac{dy}{dx}$.
$\frac{dy}{dx} = \frac{-2x}{2y} = -\frac{x}{y}$	Now make $\frac{dy}{dx}$ the subject of the expression.

EXAMPLE 2

- If $x^3 + x^2y + y^3 = 12$, find an expression for $\frac{dy}{dx}$.

SOLUTION

$\frac{d}{dx}(x^2y) = 2x \times y + x^2 \times \frac{dy}{dx}$ $= 2xy + x^2\frac{dy}{dx}$	The x^2y term needs to be differentiated using the product rule. This has been carried out first, before differentiating the whole expression.
$3x^2 + 2xy + x^2\frac{dy}{dx} + 3y^2\frac{dy}{dx} = 0$	The derivative of each term can now be found.
$(x^2 + 3y^2)\frac{dy}{dx} = -(3x^2 + 2xy)$ $\frac{dy}{dx} = \frac{-(3x^2 + 2xy)}{(x^2 + 3y^2)}$	The final stage is to make $\frac{dy}{dx}$ the subject of the expression.

USING IMPLICIT DIFFERENTIATION TO FIND EQUATIONS OF TANGENTS AND NORMALS

KEY POINTS AND DEFINITIONS

- Implicit differentiation can be used to find the gradient of a curve at a point. This gradient can then be used to find the equation of a tangent or normal to the curve.

EXAMPLE 1

- Find the equation of the tangent to the curve $x^2 - xy + y^2 = 7$ at the point with coordinates $(3, 2)$.

SOLUTION

$2x - x\dfrac{dy}{dx} - y + 2y\dfrac{dy}{dx} = 0$ $\dfrac{dy}{dx}(2y - x) = y - 2x$ $\dfrac{dy}{dx} = \dfrac{y - 2x}{2y - x}$	Use implicit differentiation to find an expression for $\dfrac{dy}{dx}$.
If $x = 3$ and $y = 2$, then $\dfrac{dy}{dx} = \dfrac{2 - 2 \times 3}{2 \times 2 - 3} = -4$	Substitute the values of $x = 3$ and $y = 2$ to find the gradient of the curve at the point $(3, 2)$.
$y = -4x + c$	Use the gradient to write down the equation of the tangent.
$2 = -4 \times 3 + c$ $c = 14$	Use the values of $x = 3$ and $y = 2$ to find c.
$y = -4x + 14$	State the equation of the tangent.

EXAMPLE 2

- Find the equation of the normal to the curve with equation $x + x^2y + e^{2y} = 1$ at the point where the curve intersects the y-axis.

SOLUTION

$1 + x^2\dfrac{dy}{dx} + 2xy + 2e^{2y}\dfrac{dy}{dx} = 0$ $\dfrac{dy}{dx}(x^2 + 2e^{2y}) = -(1 + 2xy)$ $\dfrac{dy}{dx} = \dfrac{-(1 + 2xy)}{x^2 + 2e^{2y}}$	Differentiate using implicit differentiation and make $\dfrac{dy}{dx}$ the subject of the expression.
$x = 0$ so $0 + 0 \times y + e^{2y} = 1$ $e^{2y} = 1$ $y = 0$	When the curve intersects the y-axis, $x = 0$. Use this value and the original equation to find the value of y. Remember that $e^0 = 1$.
$\dfrac{dy}{dx} = \dfrac{-(1 + 0)}{0 + 2} = -\dfrac{1}{2}$	Substitute $x = 0$ and $y = 0$ to find the gradient of the curve when it intersects the y-axis.
$y = 2x + c$	Write down the equation of the normal remembering that its gradient is $\dfrac{-1}{-\frac{1}{2}} = 2$.
$0 = 0 + c$ $c = 0$	Find the value of c using $x = 0$ and $y = 0$.
$y = 2x$	State the equation.

PARAMETRIC DIFFERENTIATION

KEY POINTS AND DEFINITIONS

- Parametric differentiation is used when expressions for x and y are given in terms of a parameter t.

MUST REMEMBER ...

$$\frac{dy}{dx} = \frac{dy}{dt} \Big/ \frac{dx}{dt}$$

EXAMPLE 1

- Given that $x = t^3$ and that $y = t + t^2$, find an expression for $\frac{dy}{dx}$.

  Hence find the values of t for which $\frac{dy}{dx} = 5$.

SOLUTION

$\frac{dy}{dt} = 1 + 2t$ and $\frac{dx}{dt} = 3t^2$	First find $\frac{dy}{dt}$ and $\frac{dx}{dt}$.
$\frac{dy}{dx} = \frac{1 + 2t}{3t^2}$	Use $\frac{dy}{dx} = \frac{dy}{dt} \Big/ \frac{dx}{dt}$.
$\frac{1 + 2t}{3t^2} = 5$	Form the equation $\frac{dy}{dx} = 5$.
$1 + 2t = 15t^2$ $15t^2 - 2t - 1 = 0$ $(5t + 1)(3t - 1) = 0$ $t = -\frac{1}{5}$ or $t = \frac{1}{3}$	Solve the equation to find the possible values of t.

EXAMPLE 2

- Given that $x = \sin^4 t$ and $y = \cos^2 t$, show that $\frac{dy}{dx} = -\frac{1 + \cot^2 t}{2}$.

SOLUTION

$\frac{dy}{dt} = -2\cos t \sin t$ and $\frac{dx}{dt} = 4\sin^3 t \cos t$	First find $\frac{dy}{dt}$ and $\frac{dx}{dt}$, by using the chain rule.
$\frac{dy}{dx} = \frac{-2\cos t \sin t}{4\sin^3 t \cos t}$ $= \frac{-1}{2\sin^2 t}$	Use $\frac{dy}{dx} = \frac{dy}{dt} \Big/ \frac{dx}{dt}$ and cancel out terms to simplify.
$= -\frac{1}{2}\csc^2 t$ $= -\frac{1 + \cot^2 t}{2}$	Remember that $\frac{1}{\sin t} = \csc t$ and use the identity $1 + \cot^2 t = \csc^2 t$.

USING PARAMETRIC DIFFERENTIATION TO FIND THE EQUATIONS OF TANGENTS AND NORMALS

KEY POINTS AND DEFINITIONS

- Parametric differentiation can be used to find the gradient at a point on a curve. This can then be used to find the equation of a tangent or a normal at that point.

EXAMPLE

- A curve is defined by $x = 36t - t^2$ and $y = 2t^3 + 2t^2$.

  (a) Find the equation of the tangent to the curve at the point where t = 2.

  (b) A second tangent has the same gradient. Find the equation of this tangent.

SOLUTION

(a) $\dfrac{dx}{dt} = 36 - 2t$ and $\dfrac{dy}{dt} = 6t^2 + 4t$	First differentiate x and y with respect to t.
$\dfrac{dy}{dx} = \dfrac{6t^2 + 4t}{36 - 2t}$	Use $\dfrac{dy}{dx} = \dfrac{dy}{dt} \Big/ \dfrac{dx}{dt}$.
When $t = 2$, $\dfrac{dy}{dx} = \dfrac{6 \times 2^2 + 4 \times 2}{36 - 2 \times 2} = \dfrac{32}{32} = 1$	Substitute $t = 2$ to find the gradient at this point.
$y = x + c$	Use the fact that the gradient is 1 to write down an equation for the line.
When $t = 2$, $x = 36 \times 2 - 2^2 = 68$ and $y = 2 \times 2^3 + 2 \times 2^2 = 16 + 8 = 24$	Find the coordinates of the point on the line where $t = 2$.
$24 = 68 + c$ $c = 24 - 68 = -44$	Find the value of the unknown c in the equation.
$y = x - 44$	State the final answer.
(b) $\dfrac{6t^2 + 4t}{36 - 2t} = 1$	If there is another value of t for which there is a tangent with the same gradient, it must satisfy the equation $\dfrac{dy}{dx} = 1$.
$6t^2 + 4t = 36 - 2t$ $6t^2 + 6t - 36 = 0$ $t^2 + t - 6 = 0$ $(t - 2)(t + 3) = 0$ $t = 2$ or $t = -3$	Solve this equation to find two values of t.
When $t = -3$, $x = 36 \times (-3) - (-3)^2 = -117$ and $y = 2 \times (-3)^3 + 2 \times (-3)^2 = -54 + 18 = -36$	Use the new value to find the coordinates of the point on the curve for this value of t.
$y = x + c$	State the form of the equation of the tangent.
$-36 = -117 + c$ $c = -36 + 117 = 81$	Find the unknown value of c.
$y = x + 81$	State the final equation.

PARTIAL FRACTIONS AND INTEGRATION I

KEY POINTS AND DEFINITIONS

- Partial fractions are often needed to simplify expressions before they are integrated.

- Logarithms are often introduced as part of the integration and their laws must be applied.

MUST REMEMBER ...

$$\int \frac{1}{ax + b}\,dx = \frac{1}{a}\ln(ax + b) + c$$

The laws of logarithms:

$$\log a + \log b = \log ab$$

$$\log a - \log b = \log\left(\frac{a}{b}\right)$$

$$n\log a = \log a^n$$

EXAMPLE

- Show that $\displaystyle\int_{2}^{4} \frac{2}{(x + 4)(2x + 3)}\,dx = \frac{2}{5}\ln\left(\frac{p}{q}\right)$,

  where p and q have no common factors.

SOLUTION

$\dfrac{2}{(x + 4)(2x + 3)} = \dfrac{A}{(x + 4)} + \dfrac{B}{(2x + 3)}$	Select the correct form of the partial fractions.
$2 = A(2x + 3) + B(x + 4)$	Compare the numerators (tops) of the fractions.
If $x = -1.5$, $2 = 2.5B$, so $B = \dfrac{4}{5}$. If $x = -4$, $2 = -5A$, so $A = -\dfrac{2}{5}$.	Substitute $x = -1.5$ to find the value of B and $x = -4$ to find A. Keep these values as fractions.
$\dfrac{2}{(x + 4)(2x + 3)} = \dfrac{4}{5(2x + 3)} - \dfrac{2}{5(x + 4)}$	
$\displaystyle\int_{2}^{4} \frac{2}{(x + 4)(2x + 3)}\,dx = \int_{2}^{4}\left(\frac{4}{5(2x + 3)} - \frac{2}{5(x + 4)}\right)dx$	Rewrite the integral using the partial fractions.
$= \left[\dfrac{4}{10}\ln(2x + 3) - \dfrac{2}{5}\ln(x + 4)\right]_{2}^{4}$ $= \left(\dfrac{2}{5}\ln 11 - \dfrac{2}{5}\ln 8\right) - \left(\dfrac{2}{5}\ln 7 - \dfrac{2}{5}\ln 6\right)$	Integrate and then substitute both limits of integration.
$= \dfrac{2}{5}(\ln 11 - \ln 8 - \ln 7 + \ln 6)$ $= \dfrac{2}{5}(\ln 66 - \ln 56)$ $= \dfrac{2}{5}\ln\left(\dfrac{66}{56}\right)$ $= \dfrac{2}{5}\ln\left(\dfrac{33}{28}\right)$	Note that $\dfrac{2}{5}$ is a factor and then simplify, using the laws of logarithms, to obtain a result in the required format.

PARTIAL FRACTIONS AND INTEGRATION II

KEY POINTS AND DEFINITIONS

- When there is a repeated factor, a term of the form
  $\dfrac{A}{(ax+b)^2}$ is obtained.

- When this is integrated, using integration by substitution,
  $\displaystyle\int \dfrac{A}{(ax+b)^2}dx = \dfrac{-A}{a(ax+b)} + c$ is obtained.

MUST REMEMBER ...

$\displaystyle\int \dfrac{1}{ax+b}dx = \dfrac{1}{a}\ln(ax+b) + c,$

$\displaystyle\int \dfrac{A}{(ax+b)^2}dx = \dfrac{-A}{a(ax+b)} + c$

The laws of logarithms:

$\log a + \log b = \log ab$

$\log a - \log b = \log\left(\dfrac{a}{b}\right)$

$n\log a = \log a^n$

EXAMPLE

- Find $\displaystyle\int_1^2 \dfrac{2x+1}{x(3x+1)^2}dx$, giving your answer in the form $\ln a - b$,

  where a and b are expressed as fractions.

SOLUTION

$\dfrac{2x+1}{x(3x+1)^2} = \dfrac{A}{x} + \dfrac{B}{3x+1} + \dfrac{C}{(3x+1)^2}$	Select the appropriate partial fractions format.
$2x+1 = A(3x+1)^2 + Bx(3x+1) + Cx$	Simplify the numerators.
If $x = 0$, then $A = 1$. If $x = -\dfrac{1}{3}$, then $\dfrac{1}{3} = -\dfrac{1}{3}C$, so $C = -1$	Substitute $x = 0$ and $x = -\dfrac{1}{3}$ to find A and C.
Comparing the coefficients of x^2 gives $0 = 9A + 3B$ $B = -3A = -3$	Find and compare the coefficients of x^2 to find B.
$\displaystyle\int_1^2 \dfrac{2x+1}{x(3x+1)^2}dx = \int_1^2\left(\dfrac{1}{x} - \dfrac{3}{(3x+1)} - \dfrac{1}{(3x+1)^2}\right)dx$	Rewrite the integral using the partial fractions.
$= \left[\ln x - \ln(3x+1) + \dfrac{1}{3(3x+1)}\right]_1^2$	Carry out the integration.
$= \left(\ln 2 - \ln 7 + \dfrac{1}{21}\right) - \left(\ln 1 - \ln 4 + \dfrac{1}{12}\right)$ $= \ln 2 + \ln 4 - \ln 7 + \dfrac{1}{21} - \dfrac{1}{12}$ $= \ln 8 - \ln 7 + \dfrac{4}{84} - \dfrac{7}{84}$ $= \ln\left(\dfrac{8}{7}\right) - \dfrac{3}{84}$ $= \ln\left(\dfrac{8}{7}\right) - \dfrac{1}{28}$	Substitute the limits of integration and simplify the result, using the fact that $\ln 1 = 0$. Keep all the numbers as fractions throughout the working.

AQA C4 · Edexcel C4 · OCR C4 · OCR(MEI) C4 · WJEC C4

UNIT VECTORS AND COLUMN VECTORS

KEY POINTS AND DEFINITIONS

- The unit vectors are **i**, **j** and **k**.

- All unit vectors have magnitude (or length) 1. The unit vectors, **i**, **j** and **k** are all perpendicular. For example, **i** could be east, **j** could be north and **k** could be vertically upwards. A system of unit vectors is shown in the diagram:

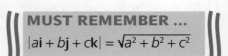

- A vector of length 6 in the **i** direction is written as 6**i**. Any vector can be expressed in the form $a\mathbf{i} + b\mathbf{j} + c\mathbf{k}$.

- Vectors of the form $a\mathbf{i} + b\mathbf{j} + c\mathbf{k}$ can also be written as column vectors, using the convention shown below.

$$a\mathbf{i} + b\mathbf{j} + c\mathbf{k} = \begin{pmatrix} a \\ b \\ c \end{pmatrix}$$

- The length of the vector $a\mathbf{i} + b\mathbf{j} + c\mathbf{k}$ is found using Pythagoras' Theorem in three dimensions. The length is given by $\sqrt{a^2 + b^2 + c^2}$.

> **MUST REMEMBER ...**
> $|a\mathbf{i} + b\mathbf{j} + c\mathbf{k}| = \sqrt{a^2 + b^2 + c^2}$

EXAMPLE 1

- Write the vector $5\mathbf{i} - 6\mathbf{j} - 8\mathbf{k}$ as a column vector.

SOLUTION

$5\mathbf{i} - 6\mathbf{j} - 8\mathbf{k} = \begin{pmatrix} 5 \\ -6 \\ -8 \end{pmatrix}$	Remember to include the negative signs.

EXAMPLE 2

- **(a)** Write the vector $\begin{pmatrix} 3 \\ -4 \\ 7 \end{pmatrix}$ in the form $a\mathbf{i} + b\mathbf{j} + c\mathbf{k}$.

  (b) Calculate the length of this vector.

SOLUTION

(a) $\begin{pmatrix} 3 \\ -4 \\ 7 \end{pmatrix} = 3\mathbf{i} - 4\mathbf{j} + 7\mathbf{k}$	Use the standard convention.
(b) $\lvert 3\mathbf{i} - 4\mathbf{j} + 7\mathbf{k} \rvert = \sqrt{3^2 + (-4)^2 + 7^2}$ $= \sqrt{74}$ $= 8.60$ (to 3 s.f.)	Use the formula for the length of a vector.

VECTORS – ADDITION AND MULTIPLICATION BY A SCALAR

KEY POINTS AND DEFINITIONS

- When working with vectors, must be able to add vectors and multiply them by scalars.

- Both forms of vectors may appear. The key results are listed below.

> **MUST REMEMBER ...**
>
> If $\mathbf{a} = \begin{pmatrix} a_1 \\ a_2 \\ a_3 \end{pmatrix}$ and $\mathbf{b} = \begin{pmatrix} b_1 \\ b_2 \\ b_3 \end{pmatrix}$, then $\mathbf{a} + \mathbf{b} = \begin{pmatrix} a_1 + b_1 \\ a_2 + b_2 \\ a_3 + b_3 \end{pmatrix}$ and $k\mathbf{a} = \begin{pmatrix} ka_1 \\ ka_2 \\ ka_3 \end{pmatrix}$.
>
> If $a = a_1\mathbf{i} + a_2\mathbf{j} + a_3\mathbf{k}$ and $b = b_1\mathbf{i} + b_2\mathbf{j} + b_3\mathbf{k}$,
>
> then $\mathbf{a} + \mathbf{b} = (a_1 + b_1)\mathbf{i} + (a_2 + b_2)\mathbf{j} + (a_3 + b_3)\mathbf{k}$ and $k\mathbf{a} = ka_1\mathbf{i} + ka_2\mathbf{j} + ka_3\mathbf{k}$.

EXAMPLE 1

- Given that $\mathbf{a} = \begin{pmatrix} 2 \\ 3 \\ -7 \end{pmatrix}$ and $\mathbf{b} = \begin{pmatrix} -1 \\ 3 \\ 5 \end{pmatrix}$, find **(a)** 5a **(b)** a − b **(c)** 4a + 3b.

SOLUTION

(a) $5\mathbf{a} = 5\begin{pmatrix} 2 \\ 3 \\ -7 \end{pmatrix} = \begin{pmatrix} 5 \times 2 \\ 5 \times 3 \\ 5 \times (-7) \end{pmatrix} = \begin{pmatrix} 10 \\ 15 \\ -35 \end{pmatrix}$	Multiply each value in the vector by 5.
(b) $\mathbf{a} - \mathbf{b} = \begin{pmatrix} 2 \\ 3 \\ -7 \end{pmatrix} - \begin{pmatrix} -1 \\ 3 \\ 5 \end{pmatrix} = \begin{pmatrix} 2 - (-1) \\ 3 - 3 \\ -7 - 5 \end{pmatrix} = \begin{pmatrix} 3 \\ 0 \\ -12 \end{pmatrix}$	Subtract each value in **b** from the corresponding value in **a**.
(c) $4\mathbf{a} + 3\mathbf{b} = 4\begin{pmatrix} 2 \\ 3 \\ -7 \end{pmatrix} + 3\begin{pmatrix} -1 \\ 3 \\ 5 \end{pmatrix} = \begin{pmatrix} 8 \\ 12 \\ -28 \end{pmatrix} + \begin{pmatrix} -3 \\ 9 \\ 15 \end{pmatrix} = \begin{pmatrix} 5 \\ 21 \\ -13 \end{pmatrix}$	Multiply **a** by 4 and **b** by 3 and then add the two vectors.

EXAMPLE 2

- If $\mathbf{a} = 2\mathbf{i} + 6\mathbf{j} - 9\mathbf{k}$ and $3\mathbf{a} + 2\mathbf{b} = 4\mathbf{i} - 4\mathbf{j} + 8\mathbf{k}$, find **b**.

SOLUTION

$3(2\mathbf{i} + 6\mathbf{j} - 9\mathbf{k}) + 2\mathbf{b} = 4\mathbf{i} - 4\mathbf{j} + 8\mathbf{k}$ $6\mathbf{i} + 18\mathbf{j} - 27\mathbf{k} + 2\mathbf{b} = 4\mathbf{i} - 4\mathbf{j} + 8\mathbf{k}$	First substitute $\mathbf{a} = 2\mathbf{i} + 6\mathbf{j} - 9\mathbf{k}$ in the equation containing **b**.
$2\mathbf{b} = 4\mathbf{i} - 4\mathbf{j} + 8\mathbf{k} - (6\mathbf{i} + 18\mathbf{j} - 27\mathbf{k})$ $= -2\mathbf{i} - 22\mathbf{j} + 35\mathbf{k}$	Make 2**b** the subject of the equation.
$\mathbf{b} = -\mathbf{i} - 11\mathbf{j} + \frac{35}{2}\mathbf{k}$	Divide by 2, to find **b**.

POSITION VECTORS

KEY POINTS AND DEFINITIONS

- The position vector of a point in three dimensional space is a vector that begins at the origin and ends at the point. The letter **r** is usually used to denote the position vector of a point.

- The diagram shows the unit vectors, **i**, **j** and **k**, and the position vector, **r**, of the point A where $\mathbf{r} = a\mathbf{i} + b\mathbf{j} + c\mathbf{k}$.

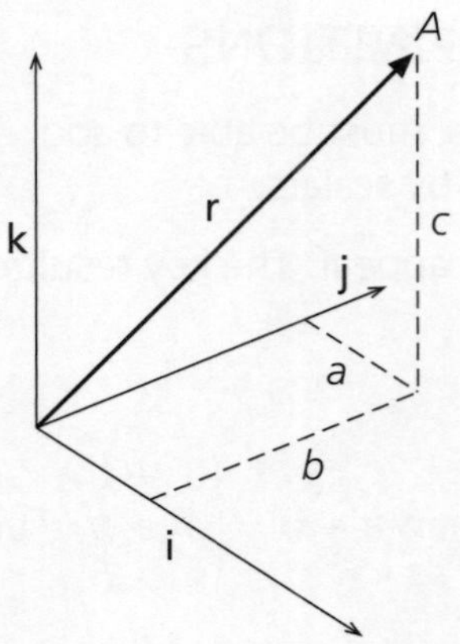

MUST REMEMBER ...

The length of the position vector $\mathbf{r} = a\mathbf{i} + b\mathbf{j} + c\mathbf{k}$ is given by $\sqrt{a^2 + b^2 + c^2}$.

EXAMPLE 1

- The point A has position vector $\mathbf{r} = 2\mathbf{i} + 8\mathbf{j} + 7\mathbf{k}$. Calculate the distance of this point from the origin.

SOLUTION

Distance $= \sqrt{2^2 + 8^2 + 7^2}$	Calculate the length of the vector.
$\qquad = \sqrt{117}$	
$\qquad = 3\sqrt{13}$	
$\qquad = 10.8$ (to 3 s.f.)	

EXAMPLE 2

- The point A has position vector $\mathbf{r}$, where $\mathbf{r} = \begin{pmatrix} 3 \\ 2 \\ k \end{pmatrix}$.

The distance of the point A from the origin is 9. Find the two possible values of k and the corresponding position vectors of A.

SOLUTION

$\sqrt{3^2 + 2^2 + k^2} = 9$	Use the length to write down an equation.
$13 + k^2 = 81$	Square both sides and solve the resulting equation.
$k^2 = 68$	
$k = \pm\sqrt{68}$	
$\quad = \pm 2\sqrt{17}$	
$\mathbf{r} = \begin{pmatrix} 3 \\ 2 \\ 2\sqrt{17} \end{pmatrix}$ or $\mathbf{r} = \begin{pmatrix} 3 \\ 2 \\ -2\sqrt{17} \end{pmatrix}$	Write down the two possibilities for $\mathbf{r}$.

DISTANCES BETWEEN POINTS

KEY POINTS AND DEFINITIONS

- If two points, A and B, have position vectors $\mathbf{a}$ and $\mathbf{b}$ respectively, then the vector from point A to B is given by $\mathbf{b} - \mathbf{a}$, as shown in the diagram.

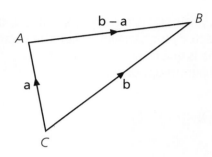

$$\overrightarrow{AB} = -\mathbf{a} + \mathbf{b} = \mathbf{b} - \mathbf{a}$$

AQA
C4

Edexcel
C4

OCR
C4

OCR(MEI)
C4

WJEC
C4

EXAMPLE 1

- The points P and Q have position vectors

$$\mathbf{p} = \begin{pmatrix} 3 \\ 6 \\ 7 \end{pmatrix} \text{ and } \mathbf{q} = \begin{pmatrix} 9 \\ 1 \\ -2 \end{pmatrix} \text{ respectively.}$$

(a) Find the vector $\overrightarrow{PQ}$.

(b) Find the distance between P and Q.

SOLUTION

(a) $\overrightarrow{PQ} = \mathbf{q} - \mathbf{p} = \begin{pmatrix} 9 \\ 1 \\ -2 \end{pmatrix} - \begin{pmatrix} 3 \\ 6 \\ 7 \end{pmatrix} = \begin{pmatrix} 6 \\ -5 \\ -9 \end{pmatrix}$	The required vector is $\mathbf{q} - \mathbf{p}$.
(b) Distance $= \sqrt{6^2 + (-5)^2 + (-9)^2}$ $\qquad = \sqrt{142}$ $\qquad = 11.9$ (3 s.f.)	Then find the magnitude of the vector between the two points.

EXAMPLE 2

- The points A and B have position vectors $\mathbf{r}_A = \mathbf{i} - \mathbf{j} + \mathbf{k}$ and $\mathbf{r}_B = 5\mathbf{i} - 6\mathbf{j} + 2\mathbf{k}$. Find the distance between the points A and B.

SOLUTION

$\mathbf{r}_B - \mathbf{r}_A = (5\mathbf{i} - 6\mathbf{j} + 2\mathbf{k}) - (\mathbf{i} - \mathbf{j} + \mathbf{k})$ $\qquad = 5\mathbf{i} - 6\mathbf{j} + 2\mathbf{k} - \mathbf{i} + \mathbf{j} - \mathbf{k}$ $\qquad = 4\mathbf{i} - 5\mathbf{j} + \mathbf{k}$	Find the vector $\overrightarrow{AB}$ or alternatively find $\overrightarrow{BA} = \mathbf{r}_A - \mathbf{r}_B$.
Distance $= \sqrt{4^2 + (-5)^2 + 1^2}$ $\qquad = \sqrt{42}$ $\qquad = 6.48$ (3 s.f.)	Find the magnitude of the vector between the two points.

THE VECTOR EQUATION OF A LINE I

KEY POINTS AND DEFINITIONS

- If the point A with position vector **a** lies on a line and the vector **d** is directed along the line, then the vector equation of the line is given by $\mathbf{r} = \mathbf{a} + \lambda\mathbf{d}$. This is illustrated in the diagram opposite.

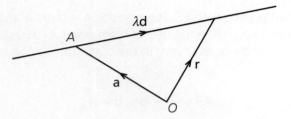

MUST REMEMBER ...

$\mathbf{r} = \mathbf{a} + \lambda\mathbf{d}$

EXAMPLE

- A line passes through the point with position vector $\begin{pmatrix} 2 \\ 7 \\ 1 \end{pmatrix}$ and is parallel to the vector $\begin{pmatrix} 1 \\ 3 \\ -2 \end{pmatrix}$.

  (a) Find the vector equation of the line.

  (b) Find the values of **a** and **b** if the point with position vector $\begin{pmatrix} a \\ a \\ b \end{pmatrix}$ lies on the line.

SOLUTION

(a) $\mathbf{r} = \begin{pmatrix} 2 \\ 7 \\ 1 \end{pmatrix} + \lambda \begin{pmatrix} 1 \\ 3 \\ -2 \end{pmatrix} = \begin{pmatrix} 2 + \lambda \\ 7 + 3\lambda \\ 1 - 2\lambda \end{pmatrix}$	Use the formula $\mathbf{r} = \mathbf{a} + \lambda\mathbf{d}$ to write down the vector equation of the line. If a vector is parallel to a line it will have the same direction as the line.
(b) If $\begin{pmatrix} a \\ a \\ b \end{pmatrix} = \begin{pmatrix} 2 + \lambda \\ 7 + 3\lambda \\ 1 - 2\lambda \end{pmatrix}$ $2 + \lambda = 7 + 3\lambda$	For the point to lie on the line, the first two entries in the vector must be equal. This gives an equation.
$-5 = 2\lambda$ $\lambda = -\dfrac{5}{2}$ $a = 2 + \lambda$ $\quad = 2 + \left(-\dfrac{5}{2}\right)$ $\quad = -\dfrac{1}{2}$	Solve the equation to find λ. Then substitute this value into the first entry in the vector to find a.
$b = 1 - 2\lambda$ $\quad = 1 - 2 \times \left(-\dfrac{5}{2}\right)$ $\quad = 6$	Substitute the value of λ into the third entry in the vector to find b.

THE VECTOR EQUATION OF A LINE II

KEY POINTS AND DEFINITIONS

- If the points A and B with position vectors $\mathbf{a}$ and $\mathbf{b}$ respectively lie on a line, then the vector equation of the line is given by $\mathbf{r} = \mathbf{a} + \lambda(\mathbf{b} - \mathbf{a}) = \mathbf{a}(1 - \lambda) + \lambda\mathbf{b}$. This is illustrated in the diagram opposite.

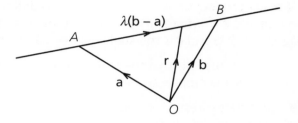

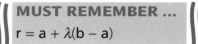

MUST REMEMBER ...

$\mathbf{r} = \mathbf{a} + \lambda(\mathbf{b} - \mathbf{a})$

EXAMPLE

- A line passes through the points A and B which have position vectors $\mathbf{a} = 5\mathbf{i} - 2\mathbf{j} + 4\mathbf{k}$ and $\mathbf{b} = \mathbf{i} + 7\mathbf{j} - 6\mathbf{k}$ respectively.

  (a) Find the vector equation of the line through these two points.

  (b) Show that the point C with position vector $\mathbf{c} = -19\mathbf{i} + 52\mathbf{j} - 56\mathbf{k}$ lies on the line.

  (c) If the point D with position vector $\mathbf{d} = p\mathbf{i} + q\mathbf{j} + 2p\mathbf{k}$ lies on the line, find the value of q.

SOLUTION

(a) $\mathbf{b} - \mathbf{a} = (\mathbf{i} + 7\mathbf{j} - 6\mathbf{k}) - (5\mathbf{i} - 2\mathbf{j} + 4\mathbf{k})$ $= -4\mathbf{i} + 9\mathbf{j} - 10\mathbf{k}$	First find $\mathbf{b} - \mathbf{a}$.
$\mathbf{r} = (5\mathbf{i} - 2\mathbf{j} + 4\mathbf{k}) + \lambda(-4\mathbf{i} + 9\mathbf{j} - 10\mathbf{k})$ $= (5 - 4\lambda)\mathbf{i} + (9\lambda - 2)\mathbf{j} + (4 - 10\lambda)\mathbf{k}$	Then apply the formula $\mathbf{r} = \mathbf{a} + \lambda(\mathbf{b} - \mathbf{a})$.
(b) $5 - 4\lambda = -19$ $-4\lambda = -24$ $\lambda = \dfrac{-24}{-4} = 6$	Use the fact that the $\mathbf{i}$ component is -19 to find λ.
$9\lambda - 2 = 9 \times 6 - 2 = 52$	Check that this value of λ gives the correct $\mathbf{j}$ component.
$4 - 10\lambda = 4 - 10 \times 6 = -56$	Check that this value of λ gives the correct $\mathbf{k}$ component.
Therefore the point C lies on the line.	State the conclusion.
(c) $p = 5 - 4\lambda$ and $2p = 4 - 10\lambda$ $10 - 8\lambda = 4 - 10\lambda$	Express p and $2p$ in terms of λ. Then form an equation from this information.
$6 = -2\lambda$ $\lambda = \dfrac{6}{-2} = -3$	Solve the equation to find λ.
$q = 9\lambda - 2 = 9 \times (-3) - 2 = -29$	Use this value of λ to find q.

THE SCALAR PRODUCT

KEY POINTS AND DEFINITIONS

- The scalar product of two vectors **a** and **b** is defined as
  $\mathbf{a.b} = |\mathbf{a}||\mathbf{b}|\cos\theta$, where $|\mathbf{a}|$ is the magnitude of **a**, $|\mathbf{b}|$ is the magnitude of **b** and θ is the angle between **a** and **b**.

- An important result is that the scalar product of two perpendicular vectors is always zero, since $\cos 90° = 0$.

- If **a** and **b** are expressed as column vectors, the scalar product can also be calculated using
  $$\begin{pmatrix} a_1 \\ a_2 \\ a_3 \end{pmatrix} . \begin{pmatrix} b_1 \\ b_2 \\ b_3 \end{pmatrix} = a_1b_1 + a_2b_2 + a_3b_3$$

- When working with the unit vectors **i**, **j** and **k**, must remember that $\mathbf{i.i} = \mathbf{j.j} = \mathbf{k.k} = 1$ and that $\mathbf{i.j} = \mathbf{i.k} = \mathbf{j.k} = 0$.

> ### MUST REMEMBER ...
>
> $\mathbf{a.b} = |\mathbf{a}||\mathbf{b}|\cos\theta$
> $$\begin{pmatrix} a_1 \\ a_2 \\ a_3 \end{pmatrix} . \begin{pmatrix} b_1 \\ b_2 \\ b_3 \end{pmatrix} = a_1b_1 + a_2b_2 + a_3b_3$$

EXAMPLE 1

- **(a)** Find the scalar product of the vectors **a** = 4**i** + 9**j** − 6**k** and **b** = 3**i** + 2**j** + 5**k**.

  (b) What can you conclude about these vectors?

SOLUTION

(a) $\mathbf{a} = \begin{pmatrix} 4 \\ 9 \\ -6 \end{pmatrix}$ and $\mathbf{b} = \begin{pmatrix} 3 \\ 2 \\ 5 \end{pmatrix}$	It is easier to find the scalar product if the vectors are in the column vector format.
$\mathbf{a.b} = \begin{pmatrix} 4 \\ 9 \\ -6 \end{pmatrix} . \begin{pmatrix} 3 \\ 2 \\ 5 \end{pmatrix}$ $= 4 \times 3 + 9 \times 2 + (-6) \times 5$ $= 12 + 18 - 30$ $= 0$	Use the formula to find the value of the scalar product.
(b) The vectors **a** and **b** are perpendicular.	Use the fact that the scalar product is zero.

EXAMPLE 2

- Show that the vectors $\begin{pmatrix} a \\ 2a \\ -2a \end{pmatrix}$ and $\begin{pmatrix} 4b \\ b \\ 3b \end{pmatrix}$ are perpendicular.

SOLUTION

$\begin{pmatrix} a \\ 2a \\ -2a \end{pmatrix} . \begin{pmatrix} 4b \\ b \\ 3b \end{pmatrix} = 4ab + 2ab - 6ab = 0$	Show that the scalar product is zero.
So the vectors are perpendicular.	State the conclusion.

THE ANGLE BETWEEN TWO VECTORS

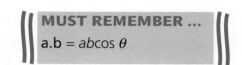

KEY POINTS AND DEFINITIONS

- The scalar product (or dot product) can be used to find the angle between two vectors.

- First calculate the scalar product, then find the magnitudes and use the formula $\mathbf{a}.\mathbf{b} = ab\cos\theta$, solving for θ.

MUST REMEMBER …

$\mathbf{a}.\mathbf{b} = ab\cos\theta$

EXAMPLE 1

- Find the angle between the two vectors $3\mathbf{i} + 4\mathbf{j} - 2\mathbf{k}$ and $4\mathbf{i} - 4\mathbf{j} + \mathbf{k}$.

SOLUTION

$3\mathbf{i} + 4\mathbf{j} - 2\mathbf{k} = \begin{pmatrix} 3 \\ 4 \\ -2 \end{pmatrix}$ and $4\mathbf{i} - 4\mathbf{j} + \mathbf{k} = \begin{pmatrix} 4 \\ -4 \\ 1 \end{pmatrix}$	Write each vector as a column vector.
$\begin{pmatrix} 3 \\ 4 \\ -2 \end{pmatrix}.\begin{pmatrix} 4 \\ -4 \\ 1 \end{pmatrix} = 3 \times 4 + 4 \times (-4) + (-2) \times 1 = -6$	Find the scalar product using the column vectors.
$\sqrt{3^2 + 4^2 + (-2)^2} = \sqrt{29}$ and $\sqrt{4^2 + (-4)^2 + 1^2} = \sqrt{33}$	Find the magnitude of each vector.
$-6 = \sqrt{29} \times \sqrt{33}\cos\theta$ $\cos\theta = \dfrac{-6}{\sqrt{29} \times \sqrt{33}}$	Use the formula $\mathbf{a}.\mathbf{b} = ab\cos\theta$ to find the value of $\cos\theta$.
$\theta = 101.2°$	Use a calculator to find θ.

EXAMPLE 2

- The angle between the two vectors $\begin{pmatrix} 1 \\ 2 \\ 4 \end{pmatrix}$ and $\begin{pmatrix} k \\ 3 \\ 1 \end{pmatrix}$ is 60°.
  Find the two possible values of k.

SOLUTION

$\begin{pmatrix} 1 \\ 2 \\ 4 \end{pmatrix}.\begin{pmatrix} k \\ 3 \\ 1 \end{pmatrix} = k + 6 + 4 = k + 10$	Find the scalar product, in terms of k, using the given vectors.
$\sqrt{1^2 + 2^2 + 4^2} = \sqrt{21}$ and $\sqrt{k^2 + 3^2 + 1^2} = \sqrt{k^2 + 10}$	Find the magnitude of each vector in terms of k.
$k + 10 = \sqrt{21} \times \sqrt{k^2 + 10} \times \cos 60°$	Use the formula $\mathbf{a}.\mathbf{b} = ab\cos\theta$ to form an equation.
$(k + 10)^2 = 21(k^2 + 10) \times \dfrac{1}{4}$ $17k^2 - 80k - 190 = 0$	Square both sides of the equation to form a quadratic in k.
$k = \dfrac{80 \pm \sqrt{80^2 - 4 \times 17 \times (-190)}}{2 \times 17}$ $= 6.44$ or -1.74 (to 3 s.f.)	Solve to find the two values of k.

THE PERPENDICULAR FROM A LINE TO A POINT

KEY POINTS AND DEFINITIONS

- Whenever perpendicular vectors are involved, the scalar product is very likely to be useful. If a vector, **q**, is perpendicular to a line with equation of the form $\mathbf{r} = \mathbf{a} + \lambda\mathbf{b}$, then $\mathbf{b}.\mathbf{q} = 0$.

- To find the perpendicular from a line, with equation $\mathbf{r} = \mathbf{a} + \lambda\mathbf{b}$ to a point Q with position vector **q**, first find the vector $\mathbf{r} - \mathbf{q}$, which needs to be perpendicular to the line, so that $(\mathbf{r} - \mathbf{q}).\mathbf{b} = 0$. This will give a value for λ. Substituting this into **r** gives the point on the line through which the perpendicular through Q must pass.

EXAMPLE

- The point P lies on the line l, with equation $\mathbf{r} = \begin{pmatrix} 3 \\ 4 \\ 1 \end{pmatrix} + \lambda\begin{pmatrix} 1 \\ -2 \\ 4 \end{pmatrix}$.

  The point Q has position vector $\begin{pmatrix} 10 \\ 6 \\ 16 \end{pmatrix}$.

  Find the value of λ for which the vector $\overrightarrow{QP}$ is perpendicular to the line l.

SOLUTION

$\overrightarrow{QP} = \begin{pmatrix} 3 \\ 4 \\ 1 \end{pmatrix} + \lambda\begin{pmatrix} 1 \\ -2 \\ 4 \end{pmatrix} - \begin{pmatrix} 10 \\ 6 \\ 16 \end{pmatrix}$ $= \begin{pmatrix} \lambda - 7 \\ -2\lambda - 2 \\ 4\lambda - 15 \end{pmatrix}$	Find the vector $\overrightarrow{QP}$.
$\overrightarrow{QP}.\begin{pmatrix} 1 \\ -2 \\ 4 \end{pmatrix} = 0$	Use the fact that $\overrightarrow{QP}$ is to be perpendicular to the line.
$\begin{pmatrix} \lambda - 7 \\ -2\lambda - 2 \\ 4\lambda - 15 \end{pmatrix}.\begin{pmatrix} 1 \\ -2 \\ 4 \end{pmatrix} = 0$ $\lambda - 7 - 2(-2\lambda - 2) + 4(4\lambda - 15) = 0$ $\lambda - 7 + 4\lambda + 4 + 16\lambda - 60 = 0$ $21\lambda - 63 = 0$	Evaluate the scalar product and simplify the result.
$\lambda = \dfrac{63}{21} = 3$	Solve the equation obtained to give the required value of λ.

THE SHORTEST DISTANCE OF A POINT FROM A LINE

KEY POINTS AND DEFINITIONS

- The shortest distance from a point to a line is along a vector that passes through the point and is perpendicular to the line.

EXAMPLE

- Find the shortest distance from the point Q

  which has position vector $\mathbf{q} = \begin{pmatrix} 14 \\ 24 \\ 17 \end{pmatrix}$ to the line l

  which has equation $\mathbf{r} = \begin{pmatrix} 1 \\ 2 \\ 4 \end{pmatrix} + \lambda \begin{pmatrix} 3 \\ 6 \\ 1 \end{pmatrix}$.

SOLUTION

$\mathbf{r} - \mathbf{q} = \begin{pmatrix} 1 \\ 2 \\ 4 \end{pmatrix} + \lambda \begin{pmatrix} 3 \\ 6 \\ 1 \end{pmatrix} - \begin{pmatrix} 14 \\ 24 \\ 17 \end{pmatrix}$ $= \begin{pmatrix} 3\lambda - 13 \\ 6\lambda - 22 \\ \lambda - 13 \end{pmatrix}$	Find the vector from the point to the line.
$\begin{pmatrix} 3\lambda - 13 \\ 6\lambda - 22 \\ \lambda - 13 \end{pmatrix} . \begin{pmatrix} 3 \\ 6 \\ 1 \end{pmatrix} = 0$ $3(3\lambda - 13) + 6(6\lambda - 22) + (\lambda - 13) = 0$ $9\lambda - 39 + 36\lambda - 132 + \lambda - 13 = 0$ $46\lambda - 184 = 0$	This must be perpendicular to the line.
$\lambda = \dfrac{184}{46} = 4$	Find λ.
$\mathbf{r} - \mathbf{q} = \begin{pmatrix} 3 \times 4 - 13 \\ 6 \times 4 - 22 \\ 4 - 13 \end{pmatrix}$ $= \begin{pmatrix} -1 \\ 2 \\ -9 \end{pmatrix}$	Find the vector from the point that is perpendicular to the line.
Shortest distance $= \sqrt{(-1)^2 + 2^2 + (-9)^2}$ $= \sqrt{86}$ $= 9.27$ (to 3 s.f.)	Calculate the length of the perpendicular vector.

THE INTERSECTION OF TWO LINES I

KEY POINTS AND DEFINITIONS

- When two lines intersect, the **i**, **j** and **k** components for one line must be equal to the corresponding components for the other line.

- If one line has equation $r_A = a\mathbf{i} + b\mathbf{j} + c\mathbf{k}$ and the other line has equation $r_B = d\mathbf{i} + e\mathbf{j} + f\mathbf{k}$, then $a = d$, $b = e$ and $c = f$ at the point of intersection.

EXAMPLE

- The vector equation of a line is $r_A = (4\mathbf{i} + 6\mathbf{j} - \mathbf{k}) + \lambda(9\mathbf{i} + 2\mathbf{j} + 5\mathbf{k})$.
  The equation of a second line is $r_B = (21\mathbf{i} + 4\mathbf{j} + 8\mathbf{k}) + \mu(5\mathbf{i} + 4\mathbf{j} + 3\mathbf{k})$.

  (a) Show that the lines intersect.

  (b) Find the position vector of the point of intersection.

SOLUTION

(a) $r_A = (4\mathbf{i} + 6\mathbf{j} - \mathbf{k}) + \lambda(9\mathbf{i} + 2\mathbf{j} + 5\mathbf{k})$ $= (4 + 9\lambda)\mathbf{i} + (6 + 2\lambda)\mathbf{j} + (5\lambda - 1)\mathbf{k}$ $r_B = (21\mathbf{i} + 4\mathbf{j} + 8\mathbf{k}) + \mu(5\mathbf{i} + 4\mathbf{j} + 3\mathbf{k})$ $= (21 + 5\mu)\mathbf{i} + (4 + 4\mu)\mathbf{j} + (8 + 3\mu)\mathbf{k}$	Express each position vector as the sum of three components.
$4 + 9\lambda = 21 + 5\mu \Rightarrow 9\lambda - 5\mu = 17$ $6 + 2\lambda = 4 + 4\mu \Rightarrow 2\lambda - 4\mu = -2$	Use two of the components to write down a pair of simultaneous equations.
$36\lambda - 20\mu = 68$ $\underline{10\lambda - 20\mu = -10}$ $\qquad 26\lambda = 78$ $\qquad \lambda = \dfrac{78}{26} = 3$	Solve these equations to find a value of λ.
$2\lambda - 4\mu = -2$ $6 - 4\mu = -2$ $-4\mu = -8$ $\mu = \dfrac{-8}{-4} = 2$	Then substitute to find the value of μ.
$5\lambda - 1 = 5 \times 3 - 1 = 14$ $8 + 3\mu = 8 + 3 \times 2 = 14$	Check that the values of λ and μ give the same value for the third component.
Therefore the lines intersect.	State the conclusion.
(b) $r = (4\mathbf{i} + 6\mathbf{j} - \mathbf{k}) + 3(9\mathbf{i} + 2\mathbf{j} + 5\mathbf{k})$ $= 4\mathbf{i} + 6\mathbf{j} - \mathbf{k} + 27\mathbf{i} + 6\mathbf{j} + 15\mathbf{k}$ $= 31\mathbf{i} + 12\mathbf{j} + 14\mathbf{k}$	Use one of the original position vectors to find the point of intersection.

THE INTERSECTION OF TWO LINES II

KEY POINTS AND DEFINITIONS

- When working with column vectors, if two lines intersect, then each of the three components must be equal to the corresponding component in the equation for the other line.

EXAMPLE 1

- The lines with vector equations $r_A = \begin{pmatrix} 2 \\ -4 \\ 3 \end{pmatrix} + \lambda \begin{pmatrix} 5 \\ 2 \\ -6 \end{pmatrix}$, and $r_B = \begin{pmatrix} -13 \\ -16 \\ h \end{pmatrix} + \mu \begin{pmatrix} 5 \\ 3 \\ -3 \end{pmatrix}$ intersect.

  Find the value of h and the position vector of the point of intersection.

SOLUTION

$r_A = \begin{pmatrix} 2+5\lambda \\ -4+2\lambda \\ 3-6\lambda \end{pmatrix}$ and $r_B = \begin{pmatrix} 5\mu-13 \\ 3\mu-16 \\ h-3\mu \end{pmatrix}$	Write each equation as a single vector.
$2+5\lambda = 5\mu-13$ $5\lambda-5\mu = -15$ $\lambda-\mu = -3$ and $-4+2\lambda = 3\mu-16$ $2\lambda-3\mu = -12$	Use the first two components in each vector to form a pair of simultaneous equations.
$2\lambda-3\mu = -12$ $2\lambda-2\mu = -6$ $\overline{-\mu = -6}$ so $\mu = 6$	Solve to find μ.
$\lambda-6 = -3$ $\lambda = 3$	Then find λ, by substituting.
$3-6\lambda = h-3\mu$ $3-18 = h-18$ $h = 3$	Use the third component to find h.
$r = \begin{pmatrix} 2 \\ -4 \\ 3 \end{pmatrix} + 3\begin{pmatrix} 5 \\ 2 \\ -6 \end{pmatrix} = \begin{pmatrix} 2 \\ -4 \\ 3 \end{pmatrix} + \begin{pmatrix} 15 \\ 6 \\ -18 \end{pmatrix} = \begin{pmatrix} 17 \\ 2 \\ -15 \end{pmatrix}$	Calculate the position vector of the point of intersection.

EXAMPLE 2

- Explain why the lines with equations $r_A = \begin{pmatrix} 2 \\ 4 \\ 3 \end{pmatrix} + \lambda \begin{pmatrix} 1 \\ 2 \\ 4 \end{pmatrix}$ and $r_B = \begin{pmatrix} 3 \\ 6 \\ 7 \end{pmatrix} + \mu \begin{pmatrix} 2 \\ 4 \\ 8 \end{pmatrix}$ do not intersect.

SOLUTION

$r_B = \begin{pmatrix} 3 \\ 6 \\ 7 \end{pmatrix} + \mu \begin{pmatrix} 2 \\ 4 \\ 8 \end{pmatrix} = \begin{pmatrix} 3 \\ 6 \\ 7 \end{pmatrix} + 2\mu \begin{pmatrix} 1 \\ 2 \\ 4 \end{pmatrix}$	By rearranging the second equation into this form, the connection between the two lines becomes apparent.
r_A and r_B are parallel.	As the vector multiplied by the scalar is the same they must be parallel.
As they pass through two different points they cannot intersect.	State the conclusion.

PROOF BY CONTRADICTION

AQA C3/4

Edexcel C3

OCR C3/4

OCR(MEI) C3

WJEC C3/4

KEY POINTS AND DEFINITIONS

- Proof by contradiction is a method of proof:
  - Begin by assuming that the result is false.
  - Show that the assumption leads to a contradiction.
  - Conclude that the required result is true.
- One of the most common applications of proof by contradiction is to prove that square roots, such as $\sqrt{2}$ and $\sqrt{3}$, are irrational.

EXAMPLE

- Prove that $\sqrt{2}$ is irrational.

SOLUTION

If $\sqrt{2}$ is not irrational, then it must be rational. Start by assuming that $\sqrt{2}$ is rational. It can then be written as a fraction, $\frac{p}{q}$ where the integers p and q have no common factors.	Set up the initial assumption, which should be the opposite of what needs to be proved.
Based on this assumption $\sqrt{2} = \frac{p}{q}$ $2 = \frac{p^2}{q^2}$ $2q^2 = p^2$	Square both sides of the expression.
As p^2 is even, p must also be even. Let $p = 2n$, where n is an integer.	Consider the implication of p^2 being even.
Substituting $2n$ for p in $2q^2 = p^2$ gives $2q^2 = (2n)^2$ $2q^2 = 4n^2$ $q^2 = 2n^2$	Proceed using the fact that p is even.
So q^2 is also even and so q is even. So p and q are both even.	Consider the implication of q^2 being even.
This contradicts the initial assumption that p and q have no common factors. So the initial assumption must be false.	Explain that there is a contradiction and that the initial assumption must be false.
So $\sqrt{2}$ cannot be written as a rational number and so $\sqrt{2}$ must be irrational.	State the conclusion.

DISPROOF BY COUNTEREXAMPLE

KEY POINTS AND DEFINITIONS

- This is a method for proving that a result is false.

- To use this method, find one case where the result does not hold. For example, to prove that all numbers of the form $2^n - 1$ are not prime, find one value of n for which $2^n - 1$ is not prime. In this case, using $n = 4$ gives $2^4 - 1 = 16 - 1 = 15$. As 15 is not a prime number, this is enough to show that it is not the case that all numbers of the form $2^n - 1$ are prime.

EXAMPLE 1

- A student claims that all numbers of the form $n^2 + n + 11$ are prime. Prove that this claim is false.

SOLUTION

Method 1 If $n = 1$, then $n^2 + n + 11 = 13$ which is prime. If $n = 2$, then $n^2 + n + 11 = 17$ which is prime. If $n = 3$, then $n^2 + n + 11 = 23$ which is prime. If $n = 4$, then $n^2 + n + 11 = 31$ which is prime. If $n = 5$, then $n^2 + n + 11 = 41$ which is prime. If $n = 6$, then $n^2 + n + 11 = 53$ which is prime. If $n = 7$, then $n^2 + n + 11 = 67$ which is prime. If $n = 8$, then $n^2 + n + 11 = 83$ which is prime. If $n = 9$, then $n^2 + n + 11 = 101$ which is prime. If $n = 10$, then $n^2 + n + 11 = 121 = 11^2$ and so is not prime. This case proves that not all numbers of the form $n^2 + n + 11$ are prime.	In this method, consecutive values of n are considered until one is found that does not give a prime number.
Method 2 Consider the expression $n^2 + n + 11$. If every term can be divided by the same number, then the whole expression will also be divisible by the same number. The only number that divides 11 is 11, so try $n = 11$. If $n = 11$, then $n^2 + n + 11 = 143 = 11 \times 13$ and is not prime. This case proves that not all numbers of the form $n^2 + n + 11$ are prime.	In this method, the expression is considered, to try to identify a value of n, which will give a result that is not prime.

EXAMPLE 2

- Prove that $2^x + 2x$, where x is a positive integer, is not always a multiple of 4.

SOLUTION

If $x = 1$, then $2^x + 2x = 4$, which is a multiple of 4.	Consider values of x, until a value of $2^x + 2x$ is found that is not a multiple of 4.
If $x = 2$, then $2^x + 2x = 8$, which is a multiple of 4.	
If $x = 3$, then $2^x + 2x = 14$, which is not a multiple of 4.	
This case shows that not all numbers of the form $2^x + 2x$ are multiples of 4.	State the conclusion.

INDEX